EROICA

CARL PIDOLL

*

EROICA

A NOVEL

*

Nikolaus Zmeskall von Domanovetz's Reminiscences of Beethoven

TRANSLATED BY

ANTHONY POWELL

METHUEN & CO. LTD

36 Essex Street, Strand, London W.C.2

First published as Verklungenes Spiel *by the Österreichische Verlagsanstalt, Innsbruck*

First English edition 1956

CATALOGUE NO. 178/U
PRINTED AND BOUND IN GREAT BRITAIN BY
THE CAMELOT PRESS LTD., LONDON AND SOUTHAMPTON

[1]

WHEN I was born, Maria Theresa was fighting the Third Silesian War. Now that I have three score years and ten behind me and my gout and rheumatism leave me little else to do but wait for death, Europe is enjoying the blessings of the so-called Holy Alliance. In other words, quite a few things have happened in the space of my lifetime. And since I have lived my whole life in Vienna, first as a pupil at the Theresianum, then as a student, and finally as an official of the Royal Hungarian Court Chancery attached to the imperial throne, my coign of vantage could hardly have been better. Of all my memories, however, I shall seek to record only one. It is a memory which is mine alone, and it would be a pity, I might perhaps even be lacking in my duty, were I to take it over with me into the great beyond.

Only when the narrative demands it will any reference be made to myself in these lines.

[2]

I WAS born in Hungary, on the estate that my father managed in his diligent, upright way as a minor country gentleman. When the Empress, who was also our Queen, founded the Theresianum that was so soon to win renown as an academy for the aristocratic sons of her realm, I was one of the first to be admitted to the imposing building on the Wieden. I owed this distinction to the intercession of Karl Count Palffy, who all his life remained my patron. I had long reached manhood before I discovered what had prompted him to take so much trouble on my behalf. Palffy had been in love with my mother before she became my father's wife and had been unable to marry her because of her family's inferior rank.

However, it had also been the emphatic wish of the Empress—and this has since become a hard-and-fast tradition—that in addition to the pupils who were assured from the cradle of a place there by virtue of their birth, the school should also offer an education to boys whose talent and aptitude compensated for their more modest origins. 'So that the young fellows from grand homes,' she would say, 'realise early in life that there are other things in the world besides privilege of birth. . . .'

In accordance with the founder's desire, we lived in fairly high style at the Theresianum. Though no more than ten years old when we started, we were addressed by our appropriate titles by professors and lackeys alike, and every two pupils had an apartment to themselves, consisting of a bedroom and a study. The sumptuous main building stood in an extensive park; we had our own stud and a covered riding school; and the food—I am now sorry to say—was of the same quality as that served to senior court officials. Had I not been so irrationally overfed since childhood, I might now be free of gout. Today I assume that all this luxury was ordered by the Empress to make it easier for the nabobs of her Empire to entrust their sons to a metropolitan establishment rather than to follow the custom of the day and have them coached at their own courts by specially selected teachers.

When I was fifteen and had attained senior status, a new arrival was assigned to me as a living and studying companion, in accordance with the usual practice. I was supposed to take him under my wing in the same way as an older schoolmate had previously done with me. The boy thus committed to my charge was Ernst Ferdinand

Waldstein from Dux in Bohemia, and at first I had a difficult time with him. He was both unruly and quick-tempered, and the task of gradually adapting him to the exigencies of the establishment was no easy one. He must have heartily loathed me in those early days, so often did I take him by the ears.

In one respect, however, we understood each other perfectly. I played the 'cello and he made rapid progress on the piano, so that soon, on festive occasions, we were allowed to appear in the big hall before the Empress herself. That illustrious lady took a keen interest in her foundation, and in several cases a powerful box on the ear served to perpetuate the impression she left on us early pupils.

When I left the Theresianum and went to read law at the University, I lost all immediate contact with Waldstein. Occasionally there were chance meetings at musical functions and the homes of mutual acquaintances, but he did not appear to seek my company and I, for my part, had no particular reason to desire his. Besides, he left Vienna before he had really finished his studies at the Theresianum, and I had no further news of him for several years. Until one day the story went around Vienna that Waldstein had resolved to join the Teutonic Knights. As it was known that this would involve a vow of celibacy, people could at first make neither head nor tail of his decision. They were relieved to find that Waldstein's father intended marrying him to a very wealthy lady who, besides being considerably older than himself, had little that was attractive in her nature, and that Waldstein junior had chosen the single blessedness of the Teutonic Order as the most elegant way out of an intolerable situation. It was actually rumoured that the idea was not Waldstein's at all, but had been put to him by the Order's Grand Master. This was none other than the Archduke Max, Maria Theresa's youngest son, who was a friend of Waldstein and extremely bored with life in Bonn-on-Rhine, where he had recently ascended the throne of an Elector and Archbishop. The Archduke Max was a young man who loved good food and comely women. He was even then running slightly to fat, and it is understandable that he should have seized this opportunity of transposing to his Rhineland exile, in the person of Waldstein, a fragment of the Viennese environment he missed so much. Be that as it may, it was learnt in Vienna that the Archduke Max had received the fugitive from matrimony with open arms and immediately raised him to the position of a confidant. He was even said to have made the knighting of his friend an occasion for holding extravagant banquets. These happenings caused not a few smiles in Vienna, where they were considered to be somewhat out of keeping with the circumstances.

At the time when this gossip was going round the capital, I did not suspect that Waldstein's migration to Bonn would lead to the personal relationship which is the subject of this book.

One day—it cannot have been long after the Emperor Leopold's death, for I remember Vienna being in partial court mourning at the time—my friend Karl Lichnowski received a letter from Waldstein announcing the impending arrival from Bonn of a young musician for whom he sought the Prince's patronage. It was a case of quite exceptional talent, he wrote, and he, Waldstein, had induced the Elector to grant the young man—at present a viola player in the Bonn Court orchestra—a prolonged leave in Vienna to perfect himself as a composer and pianist. Haydn, to whom the musician had been presented when the former broke his journey to London at Bonn, had been full of praise for him, and on his return it had been settled that the young man should be entrusted to him as a pupil. The Archduke was most eager to make his residence a centre of the arts, and the emergence among his musicians of what might prove to be a case of real genius was to him a welcome enough reason for attempting to have him trained to the ultimate advantage of his court. What was more, the writer added, the young man was an unusually accomplished pianist, and should Lichnowski afford him his patronage and take him into his salon, he would not only be assisting him—the young man's finances being extremely modest—but would probably be doing himself a good turn into the bargain, for Waldstein thought it likely that the young man would cause a considerable sensation.

Lichnowski did not take this letter very seriously.

'It looks very much to me,' he said, 'as if the Archduke is mainly interested in doing his friend Waldstein a favour. If he really were as impressed with the young man as Waldstein tries to make out, he could well afford to provide him with adequate travelling expenses. In a backwater like Bonn, where no serious competition exists, it's easy to appear a genius, and Waldstein was always one for making enthusiastic discoveries. . . . However, why not? I've written to say the young man is to come and see me when he arrives. We shall soon make up our own minds. —I'm wondering, by the way, if it's the same fellow who came here to see Mozart some years ago and disappeared again shortly afterwards. I remember Mozart telling me of a gloomy youth from the Rhineland coming to play to him. Mozart could do little with him. He seems to have been a queer fish—burning with ambition, but still terribly uncouth, shapeless and without any grace . . . I cannot recall his name. Perhaps Frau Mozart knows—you might ask her some time.'

But this I forgot to do. Indeed, I forgot the whole affair, until some months later Lichnowski unexpectedly said:

'He's come, by the way—Waldstein's prodigy from Bonn. . . .'

'Aha! What do you think of him? What does he look like?'

'An astonishing young man. Short, thickset, pockmarked; a round face, bulbous nose, sharp, deepset and rather piercing eyes; lank black hair; miserable clothes. He has no conversation and no manners. He almost seems to make a point of having none. A sort of Jacobin, if you ask me. Incidentally, he wanted to make straight for the piano to play me something, but I told him to come back tomorrow afternoon when I had a few connoisseurs there. You'll be coming too, of course?'

'I shall be glad to. *Is* he the same one who went to see Mozart?'

'I don't know,' said Lichnowski. 'I didn't ask. He could be, though, by the description.'

[3]

NEXT day I was rather late in reaching the Lichnowskis' palace, having been detained by my work. I made my apologies to the Princess, having obviously kept everyone else waiting. Then, after I had briefly greeted those present, one and all acquaintances or friends of mine, the young man whom we had assembled to judge was presented to me. I had the feeling that he saw no more of me than of the rest of his surroundings, of which he seemed to take little notice. Hardly had he given me his hand than he was back at the piano where he had been standing when I entered the room—taciturn, uncommunicative and almost hostile in his tension.

Then the Princess spoke. 'I think the party is complete now, Herr van Beethoven—if you would care to begin.'

Without a word, without so much as a bow of thanks in the direction of the Princess, he took his place at the keyboard, raised his eyes to the ceiling for a last, brief spell of concentration—and then crashed his hands down on the keys. The strings jangled and the whole instrument seemed to groan aloud beneath the impact of his touch. We looked at each other in consternation, and Lichnowski all but jumped to his feet to protest against such maltreatment of his costly piano. The Princess, however, laid a soothing hand on his arm, and the painful moment was over.

Almost forty years have passed since that afternoon. And of all those who were present I am the only one still living.

Nevertheless, I remember the mental processes it evoked as though it had been yesterday.

I can express them in a very few words. First I was half indignant and half amused. 'Vandal!' I thought. 'What a boorish, unbridled fellow he is!'

Then I realised he was not to be dismissed as simply as that. Quite against my will I began to be fascinated. I was annoyed with myself, feeling as if I were being assaulted. I rebelled against it, determined not to submit to such emotional jugglery. I found it humiliating that this fellow should be able to do such a thing to me.

But in the end I made no more attempt to resist and became oblivious of myself and my surroundings. Propping my elbows on my knees and burying my head in my hands, I abandoned myself utterly to the spell of the young man's playing, feeling it grow stronger and stronger as time went on.

[4]

I DO not know how long he played. Dusk was falling when he finished.

With head bowed and hands folded between his knees, he remained sitting at his keyboard, staring into space. Tangled wisps of black hair hung in his face.

No one moved or spoke.

At last, with a deep sigh, the Princess rose and went over to the piano.

'I cannot tell you how deeply you have moved us. You have truly divine inspiration. . . .'

The young man came unsteadily to his feet, supporting himself on the instrument with his left hand, and bowed low before the Princess.

By now Lichnowski had also approached.

'My dear Beethoven,' he said, taking the artist's right hand in both his own, 'that was the most amazing performance I have ever heard, pupil of Mozart though I was. Thank you very, very much! —From today onwards this house is yours—as our friend. . . .'

'Yes . . .' said Beethoven, 'you are very kind. . . . And now I beg leave to go. I cannot talk now. . . . Please excuse me. . . .'

Without waiting for a reply or paying the least heed to the rest of those present, he walked to the door. The Princess signalled to one of the footmen bringing lights in to show him the way out.

[5]

'GOOD heavens, what a boor!' someone whom I do not care to name blurted out.

'A boor perhaps,' the Princess rejoined, her voice still tense with emotion, 'but a genius too! —He will easily make good his lack of manners if only he takes the trouble. I fear that is the least of his needs. It is probably high time a little love and human warmth were brought into his life. It tugs at one's heart to sense the hardship and loneliness that surround him. . . .'

Many a time since then have I been reminded of the Princess's words.

[6]

IT is hardly worth recounting the discussion that followed. Like all discussions of its kind, it was lengthy, animated, and ultimately meaningless. None the less, not even those who could not approve of Beethoven's technique had any hesitation in acknowledging his remarkable talent. I myself kept aloof from all this, being reluctant to commit myself on things about which I was still very much perplexed.

Soon afterwards, under the pretext of having work to finish at home, I took my leave of the Princess and Lichnowski and made my way to the Bastion with the idea of taking a brisk walk to clarify my impressions.

[7]

BETWEEN me and that afternoon there now lie my entire experience of Beethoven's later work and my whole awareness of the development he subsequently went through. It is not surprising, therefore, that those first impressions of his musical personality acquired at Lichnowski's home no longer hold any mystery for me. To recapture the bewilderment that filled me at the time I must—not without some effort—turn my thoughts back to my life as a young man and my outlook on music in those far-off days.

To be sure, music had stirred me often enough before I ever met Beethoven. That almost goes without saying. But it had been a different kind of feeling—indirect and somehow almost furtive. One took pleasure in music, in its symmetry, its grave or friendly beauty; one followed the art of the maestro with inner delight or open admiration—

and, very occasionally, one experienced an unexpected but vivid thrill. This was something not to be mentioned openly; one was very nearly ashamed of it; and when—as I did—one repeatedly succumbed to this inner captivation one tended to regard it as one's own peculiar form of over-sensitivity. And as the established attitude towards music in that century was one of superior composure, such over-sensitivity placed a man on dangerous ground and he took good care not to admit to such a thing.

Since Beethoven has meanwhile taught us how to grasp the artistic sense and content of music while under the sway of this emotion, I naturally find it quite laughable today to have let myself be so disturbed by that first introduction. But I could not help it at the time. His exacting approach to his listeners was in the early stages bound to appear in the worst of taste—a tactless violation of certain sacred confines of artistic propriety, an act of Jacobin frenzy, a thing quite beyond the pale, like Schiller's *Räuber* or the confessions of Rousseau. Nowadays, perhaps, I ought to be less surprised by the way Beethoven stupified and perplexed us all on his first appearance at Lichnowski's home than by his ability—notwithstanding our bewilderment and confusion—to compel our recognition of his talent and accomplishment.

I know now that we succumbed to him then because we were ripe for the new era which he personified. I know now that Mozart and Haydn, in whose names many were first inclined to condemn Beethoven, were the very men who had brought us up to Beethoven and the directness of his approach. But I also know that I was incapable of realising this at the time and that I was quite justified in being so confused by the impression Beethoven had made on me.

I remember some of the questions I asked myself as I paced along the Bastion that evening: 'Who gives him the right to reach into people's hearts without so much as by your leave? Is it not shameless to bare oneself like that? To expose one's heart so openly to the public gaze? Does it not lead to chaos and the disintegration of all artistic form to make music as that fellow does? Does it not probably lead to a slackening of all moral restraint?'

They were all questions to which only my heart could whisper the answer—that this young man from Bonn was a genius of the highest order and that I would do better to trust in and devote myself to what he had to tell than to subject it to fruitless and foolish criticism. This, indeed, he had already compelled me to do, whether I liked it or not.

There is something else which I should not omit to recall. Just when Beethoven made his first appearance at the Lichnowskis' there was very bad news from Paris. The King had been deposed and was a prisoner in the Temple. The position of his wife, the daughter of Maria Theresa, was no better. It was whispered that both their lives were in danger, that the *Révolution* might well treat the pair as criminals and send them to the scaffold. Anyone, therefore, who realised that the young musician sent to us from Bonn by Waldstein represented a fragment of the spirit generally considered to have perpetuated the terrible events in France needed more than a little courage to disregard the associations which thereby sprang to mind. I remember only too well that Lichnowski exposed himself to violent censure from certain quarters by assisting the 'Jacobin', especially after the execution of Louis and Marie Antoinette had become a dreadful reality. One thing I do know: the impression that Beethoven's playing had left with me greatly contributed, during that walk of mine along the Bastion, to advancing a decision that had long been taking shape in my mind in relation to the new ideas and influences, dangerous though they might be, and to driving the ideals of my youth and upbringing into the background.

Quite vaguely and subconsciously as yet, I had sensed

that this man was not only a musical genius but also something quite exceptional as a human being—a man with whom it would certainly be worth my while to become more closely acquainted.

[8]

SUDDENLY I saw him before me in person. It was on the *Mölker Bastei*, where there was a bench between two tall lime trees. I caught sight of him in the twilight—bareheaded, hands clasped behind his back, gazing out over the broad plain towards the foot-hills and mountains of the *Wienerwald*.

'So you are also taking a stroll before it gets too dark?' I called out to him.

He did not answer immediately but continued to contemplate the scenery.

'A beautiful land,' he said at last. For the first time I was struck by the broadness of his Rhineland accent.

'Beautiful *and* fertile,' I told him. 'There's capital wine grown out there.'

'Is that so?' he exclaimed, turning round to face me. 'Even when one comes from my part of the world?'

I accepted the challenge. There is no Viennese in existence who is not proud of his wines.

'I will gladly prove it to you—on the spot—if you will do me the pleasure of dining with me.'

'No, thank you,' he retorted with a tartness that was almost uncivil. 'I can pay for my supper myself.'

Aha, I thought. So that was it. Aloud I answered him evenly enough: 'I don't doubt it. —But when you were playing to us earlier, I didn't tell you that I could make my own music.'

'And can you?'

'Not like you, of course, but still . . .'

'*So?* What can you do?'

'Play the 'cello and compose quartets.'

I had the impression that it would have been wrong not to lay my cards on the table. And the tone of my reply seemed to have been the appropriate one. The young man gave me a sharp, curious look and said in a much more friendly voice: 'Really? What is your name then?' I told him, explaining at the same time who I was. This information also seemed to satisfy him.

'So there is no need to be afraid of you?' he asked—albeit in a tone that was anything but timid.

'In Vienna you need fear no one who is musical,' I replied. 'In any case, music-making will be more important to you than anything else.'

'What do you mean—"more important"?' he cried. 'And more important than what? *Is* there anything else but music?'

'For those of us not so gifted as yourself, there is—unfortunately—quite a good deal else. . . .'

'Thank God you say "unfortunately",' he growled crossly. 'Otherwise your quartets could not be worth much. Nor your 'cello-playing.'

He shot me a quizzical look, as if something were amusing him.

'May I ask you something?'

'Of course.'

'After I had left Prince Lichnowski's home, wasn't there some Clever Dick or other who thought I had only played you a well-rehearsed party-piece and that when I was given definite subjects to improvise on it would soon emerge what I was really made of?'

I had to laugh.

'Oh yes, some people did say that.'

'Were you among them by any chance?' he cried.

'I was not. I'm not one of those people who are eternally afraid that someone will abuse their trust.'

Again he darted that keen look in my eye. Then he returned to his thoughts.

'Next time we meet at the Prince's home,' he said, 'just you bring the conversation round to the idea of setting me one or two themes to make sure that I am not a fraud. *Then* I shall show the company what free improvisation is!'

'Yes, but didn't you show us that today?' I asked in some astonishment.

'Not quite,' he confessed without the least embarrassment. 'Much depended on today, after all. I have a few well-tried recipes for such occasions—though they naturally do not always turn out the same. Besides, in the end I really was "free" and had lost all my anxiety. —What kind of a man is the Prince?' he inquired, *à propos* of nothing.

'Not an easy question to answer,' I told him. 'Very well-meaning, at all events. Quite free of any mistrust or touchiness. And when he enthuses over anything, he knows no bounds. But he *is* rather obstinate. I would advise you to bear that in mind.'

He made no reply, though his face showed that he was thinking over what I had just told him.

'When do you think I should go to see the Prince again?' was his next question. 'Soon? Or would it be wiser to wait?'

'You had best go straight away,' I said. 'Tomorrow.'

'Will you come too?'

'Certainly, if you do. I would not miss a single note you play.'

Once again I was aware of that keen, sidelong look which seemed to ask: 'Can I really trust you . . .?'

Then he suddenly began to move, his hands once again clenched behind his back, apparently taking for granted that I would accompany him for the rest of his walk.

'Look here, Mr. 'Cello-player,' he exclaimed, 'I intend

to do great things! I damned well mean to make all of you prick up your ears! I have things to say that no one has said before me—neither Haydn nor Mozart! And I'm going to say them in a way no one has ever done before! It's to come straight from *my* heart into *your* hearts! Nothing must stand between them! None of that infernal nonsense about form and symmetry and elegance and restraint! When a gale roars through the treetops or lightning splinters an oak trunk, they don't ask beforehand whether it's convenient or whether *Frau Baronin* would mind being disturbed. No, when I lay hold of my piano, it's time for people to be moved, and I don't waste time asking questions. I sit down and overcome you all—every single one of you! No one can elude me! And the longer, the more often you listen, the less chance you will have of doing so! Because I always have something different to tell—something new every time! And because you'll learn to understand me better and better!'

'I willingly believe that,' I said as he paused and allowed his voice to sink. 'I am sure most of us do who heard you this afternoon. The Princess was greatly moved by your playing. . . .'

'Was she?' he cried, seizing on this. 'What did she say?'

I thought for an instant.

'I shall tell you some time,' I replied. 'When we are better acquainted.'

This provoked him. 'That's the way you all are,' he shouted. 'First you tell me how my music has gripped you—and then up comes that everlasting cautiousness and mistrust. I can't possibly say anything more genuine or sincere to you than my music tells you, and if you can understand *that*, what more can you expect of me with all your cautiousness and mistrust, that "never-can-tell" attitude of yours? Oh, it's enough to drive one to despair! You've just listened to me for an hour and a half, and it hasn't so much as occured to you—a music-lover, a 'cello-player, a composer of quartets—that a man who makes music like mine deserves trust, not suspicion!'

He had worked himself into a considerable state of excitement. To me it seemed rather exaggerated and unjustified.

'The reason why I kept the Princess's remark from you,' I said with deliberate calmness, 'was not that I distrust you but because I do not know whether she would want me to pass it on.'

He seemed taken aback by this. 'You are right,' he replied quietly. 'Very right, in fact.' And then he added abruptly: 'Listen, Mr. 'Cello-player, I have taken a liking to you. If you're still serious about inviting me to supper, I shall be glad to accept.'

[9]

I TOOK the young musician to an inn on the Wieden where I often went in those days. The food and drink were good, and the place was mainly frequented by the tradespeople and artisans of the neighbourhood.

'Music makes me hungry,' said Beethoven, and to my delight he ate with a hearty appetite. Even our wine drew his praise. He allowed me to initiate him into the secrets of *Heuriger*, which is not a *Heuriger* at all but a *Vorjähriger*, and to acquaint him with the different qualities of the vines with which God had blessed our surrounding countryside.

He spoke not another serious word that evening. He was as merry as a child, drawing everyone around us into the conversation and showing himself to be a man who was not afraid of a broad joke.

About ten o'clock he suddenly announced he must go

home, having much before him on the morrow. He insisted on escorting me to my apartment—'one courtesy deserves another,' he told me—and with a warm handshake left me alone with my impressions.

[10]

Next day we had a quartet at the Lichnowskis' and were in the middle of playing a Mozart adagio when Beethoven came in. Signing to us not to bother about his presence, he quietly sat down in the background to listen—just as an old and intimate friend of the family might have done.

When we had finished he came over and said, without a word of greeting to anyone: 'A beautiful piece—and quite nicely done, too.' He then proceeded to give us a few instructions on how to bring out this or that passage a little better and, taking the viola from its player's hand, ran through a particular phrase which was not to his liking. He treated me in particular as if we had been friends for years.

Lichnowski noted this with astonishment and doubtless with a certain envy. He had been a friend of Mozart's and, as a music-lover, attached great importance to being taken seriously by musicians.

Later, with Beethoven at the piano, we played a Haydn trio. To our great surprise, in view of what we had seen of his own style of playing the day before, Beethoven did full justice to the filigreed grace of his part.

In the meantime numerous guests had been arriving. The Princess was among them, and Beethoven was at pains to greet her with the utmost amiability. A moment later he gave me the same sly nudge as might pass between two schoolboys bent on some prank together. Obviously he was in the best of moods.

Accordingly I turned to the Princess and asked whether she would mind if Herr van Beethoven played to us again. This time, I said, I would like to make his task more difficult by asking him to improvise on one or two themes set by the present company. Everyone applauded my idea, whereupon Beethoven handed me a score-pad and pencil with the request that I should get someone to note down three themes.

Having duly complied, I tore out the lead and returned it to him.

For a short while he knitted his brow over the three motifs.

'May I add one more?' he asked.

We readily agreed to this, and when he had jotted down a short motif as his fourth theme, he handed the sheet to the Prince and sat down at the piano. His performance by far surpassed that of the previous day, and I have seldom known him attain the same heights since. What his fingers brought forth was a pyrotechnic display of spirit, wit, superb gaiety and feeling—a triumph of craftsmanship for any connoisseur. He interpreted the themes we had set him in an amazing series of variations; he juggled with them like coloured balls; he whirled them to and fro in the most surprising turns of expression; and finally he improvised a perfectly controlled triple fugue which he appropriately crowned by bringing in his own motif, victorious and radiant, as a *cantus firmus*.

Even while he was playing there had been several involuntary cries of admiration from his audience. When he finished a wave of unrestrained enthusiasm swept through the room. Men and women crowded round the piano to wring his hand, none of them knowing how to thank or applaud him sufficiently for the pleasure he had given.

It was already very late when the company at long last

dispersed. And from that day on Vienna knew for sure that yet another star of supreme brilliance had risen on the horizon of her music.

Lichnowski was beside himself with delight. He went from one guest to another, declaring over and over again:

'This man will fill the place of Mozart for us! He's come to make amends for Mozart's early death! It's Mozart *redivivus*!'

He completely forgot at this moment that, in his profound and genuine grief over the premature loss of his inspired friend and teacher, he had for a whole year repeatedly assured anyone prepared to listen to him that as long as music continued to be made in this world there would never, never be another Mozart.

[11]

To my intense pleasure Beethoven kept up our happy-go-lucky comradeship in the weeks and months that followed, preserving the note of natural and—one might almost say—professional intimacy which had been struck on the first day we met. Though well aware that I had no right to such a title, he dubbed me 'the musical count' and continued to use this nickname till the end of his days.

Meanwhile, I was becoming increasingly conscious that the young man's self-confidence, which was admittedly enormous, was counter-balanced by an uncommon amount of self-discipline. Many people, while having to acknowledge his supreme talent, found this self-confidence objectionable, but I myself soon discovered that, naïve and drastic though it may have seemed at times, Beethoven's particular form of self-esteem was, at all events, quite free of vanity or narcissism. It was akin to a natural force—

indeed, it *was* a natural force, a manifestation of his personality that was neither good nor bad but just something God had given him. His discipline and self-control, on the other hand, were both hard-won moral forces and deserved full admiration.

How easily might many another man, amid that delirious, ever-mounting success, have sunk into complacency and thenceforth confined himself to exploiting his own achievements! Such a thought never entered Beethoven's head. All he saw were his deficiences, and with a modesty which weighed no less than his self-esteem he deliberately set out to extend his knowledge and improve his technique.

'I must learn everything which possibly *can* be learnt,' he told me on more than one occasion. 'I must learn to do everything anyone before me has ever been able to do—and learn to do it at least as well. How else am I to bring out all the new ideas that are striving to emerge from me?'

The practical outcome of this in the course of the next few years was that he took instruction from Haydn and later from Albrechtsberger—who had also been my teacher—and surrendered himself to the strict control of those great artists. This included submitting deliberately to disciplines which were quite at variance with his intractable nature.

'Learning,' he would say, 'doesn't mean doing things one can do already or do with ease. It means doing what one can't do or finds hard to do.'

Such statements were self-evident, logical and irrefutable enough—perhaps they even bordered on the platitudinous—but how few are the people who can remain true to such axioms, particularly when they have achieved such unusual success as Beethoven had had in his first few years in Vienna!

Many was the time he inveighed against Haydn and Albrechtsberger and applied the most atrocious names to them in my presence. He called Haydn a pedantic old woman and Albrechtsberger an insufferable slave-driver, to quote the least uncharitable of his utterances. A hundred times he swore that he was sick to death of it all, that he was subjecting himself to futile, ridiculous, miserable drudgery. But having once unburdened himself, he would sit down, grit his teeth and do what was demanded of him. Schenk, too, became his teacher, and later even Salieri, whom he found utterly repugnant. 'But he's very able,' Beethoven would say. 'He's mastered things that I find strange and don't take to easily.'

In a word: apart from admiring the young artist's genius like everyone else in Vienna, I also grew to know and respect a man imbued with a sense of duty and moral obligation—a man whom most people did not see or deliberately overlooked, either because of their often quite superficial glorification of his talent or because of his own tendency to be crotchety and abrupt. It amazed me more and more as time went on how he accepted as his due, and at the same time utterly despised, the ecstatic enthusiasm which inundated him from all sides.

'Just so many snow-geese and monkeys' were the words he once used to me as we were leaving a salon full of his devotees. 'They tumble all over each other in their admiration—and haven't the remotest idea how much I still have to learn and draw out of myself. . . .'

[12]

FRIENDLY and familiar though Beethoven was in our everyday relations, and ready though he may have been to accept any service, large or small, I was able to render him, he remained correspondingly aloof in all matters affecting his own life as a man. I soon noticed that it only made him shy and mistrustful if I tried to make him talk about himself and his earlier life. I soon gave up the attempt, resolving to satisfy my curiosity in another way. Although I had not been in close touch with Waldstein for some years, I could still fall back on our friendship of the Theresianum days. Apart from this, the question I wished to put to him concerned a person in whom he himself was, as the sponsor, keenly interested and whom he also greatly esteemed.

Knowing that the Archduke Max had had to flee from his residence in Bonn before the Revolutionary armies and was now in Münster, his second bishopric, I assumed Waldstein to be with him and wrote to him there. I described the first successes of his protégé in Vienna, told him of the impression he had made on me personally and of my warm human interest in the newcomer, and finally asked him to let me know—when he had the time and inclination—something of the man's early circumstances.

My guess proved correct. It was not long before Waldstein's answer reached me.

He began by recounting the events and experiences which had led up to the flight to Münster—in this connection it plainly emerged that his friendship with the Archduke would not last very much longer—and then he thanked me for my patronage of young Beethoven, of which he had heard from an independent party, and finally he delivered himself of a somewhat involved narrative which went far towards satisfying my curiosity.

'A recent bonmot of the Archduke's brings me straight to the subject of your inquiry,' he wrote. 'A few months ago, when he was running through the correspondence from Bonn, he looked up at me and said, raising his left eyebrow in that way of his: "The beverage tax has suffered a heavy loss, my dear friend—Herr Johann van Beethoven is dead. . . ." This same Johann van Beethoven was none other than the father of our protégé. . . .'

(I clearly remember being almost shocked to realise,

the first time I read Waldstein's letter, that Beethoven had never said a single word to me about his father's death, which must have occurred shortly after his own departure from Bonn.)

'. . . Neither was the Elector exaggerating,' Waldstein continued. 'Old Beethoven used to drink enough for six. This unhappy partiality for the bottle was eventually the death of him—but not before he had brought his entire family dangerously close to ruin. I will tell you the whole story, and since I was a witness of the sad things that happened, you could hardly hear it from a better source.

'When I first made young Beethoven's acquaintance over five years ago, his mother was still alive. She was a simple but likeable woman, overworked and careworn by her never-ending efforts to shield the family—there were three other children besides our charge, all of them younger and one still quite tiny—from the effects of her husband's drunkenness. Beethoven's father was a singer in the Elector's choir, and had the latter not been so tolerant of human weakness, the man would probably have lost his job long ago. His voice was gone and he already had a record for professional unreliability. In short, I considered our young Beethoven then a lad of fifteen or sixteen, to be living in an impossible atmosphere which was undoubtedly detrimental to his artistic talent, and I made use of the special favour that the Archduke was pleased to show me to put in a good word for my protégé. I had no great difficulty in persuading the Elector to give the young man leave of absence to be sent to Mozart with a monetary grant. That must have been in '87. Beethoven left Bonn forthwith, leaving me hopeful that by this one stroke I had cut the Gordian knot of his unhappy plight. Unfortunately he had only been gone a few months when his mother's consumption suddenly took a turn for the worse. The news must have hit the young man very hard, for without a moment's hesitation he packed his few belongings and hastened back home. Another reason, I think, for this precipitate departure was that he had failed to excite any real interest with Mozart or anyone else in Vienna and was feeling hopelessly out of place there. At the time I dashed off a letter begging him not to jeopardise his whole training and future by taking his mother's illness too seriously: if only he would stay in Vienna and adhere to his original plan, I promised, I would do everything in my power to help his mother and ensure that she went short of nothing.

'But Beethoven never received that letter. Even if it had arrived before he left, it would probably still not have shaken him in his resolve. He reached Bonn just in time to see his mother die and to bury her. He must have loved her very much, for the blow was almost too much for him.

'The worst was not to come till a few months later, though, when it became clear that the father, Johann, had now abandoned the last vestiges of self-restraint. His so-called grief over the loss of his wife was a convenient excuse for toping even more heavily than before. With the whole of its modest income now being frittered away on drink, the family was soon in the direst want.

'No sooner did I see how the land lay than I had a private talk with young Beethoven to try to make him see that things could not possibly go on like this and that I refused to stand by and watch such talent as his being wasted just because his father was incapable of showing the slightest self-control.

'Beethoven asked what I had in mind.

'The answer to that, I told him, was perfectly simple. I would ask the Elector to pension his father off and find him board and lodging with a good, reliable family. The brothers and sisters could—with the Elector's gracious permission—be committed to public institutions. As for Beethoven himself—the one person, after all, whose interest must be considered—I would have him given leave to return to Vienna immediately.

'It was then that I experienced the surprise of my life. Beethoven all but subjected me to physical assault, so convulsed was he with rage. He raved and screamed at me with tears of indignation in his eyes, asking if I were unaware that his family had enjoyed an honourable reputation in Bonn for over fifty years past! Did I imagine, in my detestable, arrogant, heartless indifference, that I could efface those fifty years at one fell swoop, destroying his family and exposing it to public shame? Did I think his mother had suffered her twenty years of martyrdom merely to have all she had done for her children wiped out in this contemptuous, overbearing fashion, before even the earth on her grave were dry?

'Believe me, it was a disagreeable scene! All my efforts to make him understand that I was thinking only of him and the furtherance of his talents were in vain. Over and over again he reviled me for being cold and insincere—a man bereft of love and human understanding. He told me plainly that with things as they were he did not give a damn for his talent; what was at stake now was honour—the honour of a whole family, the honour of his grandfather and ancestors, who had been respected and hard-working men, the honour of his brothers and sisters, who must go out into life in freedom and decency, not as beggar children from an orphanage. . . . Still fuming, he left me. For the time being I had no choice but to await developments.

'What ultimately happened was something surprisingly unemotional. A few days later there appeared on the Elector's desk a petition from young Beethoven asking for his father's salary to be paid out to him, the son, in order that it might be turned to proper account—that is, the maintenance of the family and the education of his brothers and sisters.

'The Elector was extraordinarily pleased and turned a deaf ear to my protestations about the folly of allowing talent like young Beethoven's to go to wrack and ruin in such a sordid and hopeless environment.

'It is much more important,' he said, 'to give the young man a chance to mould his character than to molly-coddle his talents. The man and his rights come first—the artist in him second. He's proud enough to want to preserve his family honour, and I'm the last to hinder him in the attempt. That young man is made of hard stuff, and he shall have his way. If his talent perishes in the process, it won't have been worth very much.'

'And there, to my great annoyance, the matter rested. The petition was granted—and young Beethoven spent five whole years ruling his father, brothers and sisters with an iron hand and augmenting his father's slender income by earnings of his own. In a word, he concentrated all his energies on ensuring that the name of Beethoven retained its bourgeois independence and respect. He worked like a madman as a relief organist, viola player, pianist and teacher, and when a serious illness confined him to his bed for a long period, he was driven almost out of his mind by rage and frustration. But he achieved his object. He accomplished the task he had set himself—and only when he saw that I had to bow to such heroic self-denial did he come forward and permit me to resume our old relationship once more.

'In that story you have all that is known about him. He has a will like steel and an indomitable pride. If it can be said of any man that he will crack but never bend, you may say it of him.

'Anything else I have to tell is of minor importance. Nevertheless, it may interest you to know that his grandfather, who worked his way up from a simple chorister to conductor of the court orchestra, seems to have had the same iron will. I am told he hailed from Flanders—either Antwerp or Malines. He came to Bonn as a young man and married there. His son's intemperance was inherited from his wife, who was also ruined by drink. The grandfather had talent, but nothing more.

'Our protégé has, by the by, many friends in Bonn, a number of them splendid people. A widowed lady called Frau von Breuning has done much on his behalf, and her sons were on good terms with him. A certain Wegeler, a gifted fellow who is reading medicine, has also had a good influence on him. The Electoral Theatre, on the other hand, has done little to refine his manners: he was quick to adopt the salacious talk of those stage people. . . .

'I shall be glad to assist you should you need any further details, but as I have said, you are already in possession of the main essentials—including the fact that Haydn's two visits brought about the final break with Bonn.

'Both brothers are growing up and well cared for. One is apprenticed to an apothecary, the other wants to be a musician but has nothing remotely approaching his brother's talent.

'*Voilà tout pour le moment*—and I trust that I have been of some help to you. . . .'

This letter and the remark by Princess Lichnowski which I mentioned previously both did much to deepen my friendship for Beethoven. Even in those early days I had already seen quite enough hollowness, insincerity, toadying and hypocrisy to appreciate the rare worth of a real man.

[13]

IT would be foolish to pretend that the young Beethoven as I knew him at twenty-two or twenty-three was not conscious of his mission. Conversely, anyone assuming that he was already clear about the nature and purport of that mission is greatly mistaken.

Today, when Beethoven has been gone for over three years and his work as a composer lies before us in its completed state, its importance, scope and greatness might well lead us to think that anyone who accomplished so much must surely have known all along that he came into the world for no other reason than to achieve the very things that Beethoven has bequeathed to us. The example of men like Mozart or Haydn, both of whom from their early childhood knew no higher aim than to distinguish themselves as composers, gives added weight to this misapprehension. In reality things were quite different with Beethoven. Though he, too, had done some composing in his early years, he did not at first believe that his main gifts lay in the creative sphere. On the contrary, in the days when I first knew him, and for some years afterwards, he sought his ultimate goal entirely in the field of the pianoforte virtuoso. This was quite understandable. His keyboard technique was so overwhelming, his limitless ability as an improvisator, as a brilliant and imaginative creator of perpetually new expressions and images so convincing, that his capacity for composition as it then was could not bear or seek comparison. His genius, so direct in its power to convince, at that time expressed itself so exclusively in piano-playing that he would have been a fool to disregard the fact.

How often did I ask him, when he had moved us to ecstasy by his playing, why he did not apply himself to recording for posterity what he had created in free improvisation? And on the few occasions when he did not crossly decline to answer my question, he would say: 'I have often tried. But it won't work. The moment I put pen to paper, a kind of paralysis seems to come over me. I have no real ideas, and what is left staring back at me from the manuscript is wooden, empty and meaningless. I can't explain why—it simply turns out that way. When you are all sitting round me, when I feel you waiting to be thrilled by my playing, when I feel your tension and anticipation—*that's* when it comes over me, *that's* when the things I have to say want to burst forth and rise up to the light. Only then do I find myself and then forget myself again, as if another person were sitting there and playing—as if another man's art were coming to life through me, regardless of my own feelings. . . .'

In fact Beethoven had long been a successful and famous musician in Vienna before anyone even dreamt that he might be anything more than an exceptionally fine pianist, virtuoso and improvisator—or even pianoforte teacher. No one could have detected the composer in him in those days, for even when engaged on composition he let no one know of it and had less intention still of publishing anything. The fact must also be recorded here that his teachers—Haydn and particularly Albrechtsberger—had no very high opinion of his gifts as a composer and commented most disparagingly on them from time to time. They thought him clumsy and lacking in suppleness, grace and finesse—'like the man who takes a sledge-hammer to crack a nut'.

At all events, three years passed before he presented his Opus I to the world and thereby gave notice of his hope to win renown as a composer. Delightful though these trios are and friendly though their reception was, it never occurred to anyone that they might be the forerunners of the outstanding composition which was to follow.

And so things remained for a number of years, till almost the turn of the century. Even when the time came for a work of Beethoven's to achieve striking success and to thrill the public at large—I refer here to the Septet first heard about 1800—all the experts still preferred to regard it as a revival of something that had ended with Mozart's early death rather than the manifestation of a genius one day destined to create something sensationally new.

Most people have forgotten this by now. They think young Beethoven always knew he would some time or other write the Third and Fifth Symphonies, Fidelio and the Missa Solemnis. I am not stressing the falseness of this assumption in order to be dogmatic or merely for the sake of historical accuracy. I do so because it takes no account of the long, arduous path which led Beethoven, the artist and the man, to those remarkable later works of his, because I see this inner development as the real meaning and purpose of his life.

[14]

IN those early years in Vienna he often proclaimed with great vehemence—and continued to do so despite all my objections—that basically speaking there was no 'respectable' form of artistic activity other than that which brings the musician face to face with his listener and shows him as he really is—as a mature man among other men, not just as a musician among music-lovers.

'Music isn't just a pleasant tinkling in the ears!' he would cry. 'Music is the language of the heart speaking to other hearts. . . . When I want to let my heart speak, when it's filled to bursting-point and about to overflow, I can't sit down to a music score and wrestle with a goose-quill and inkpot. That's the time I need to feel the presence of human beings whose hearts I can open and conquer, the time I want to have my hands on a piano that will ring out with all the things I feel. . . . How often did I envy singers and actors for being able to pass what they felt direct into the hearts of other men and women—until the day I found I could do something greater still! What I play isn't something another man has created and polished up for me in advance: I play what my emotions of the moment are telling me—and I use different sounds every time! Don't you see that there can be no higher or truer artistry than that?!'

And when I still sought to differ, he would fall back on the argument that people's emotional reactions and enthusiasm were still the best way of judging artistic performance. 'Let's see whether you can overwhelm people with a Mozart Sonata to the same extent as I can with fifteen minutes' free improvisation . . . !'

He seemed utterly possessed by the idea and never tired of declaring that he would show the world he was right. I would live to see the day, he promised, when true connoisseurs would want nothing but improvised music—once they had found this was the only kind that could not lie.

'There can't be any humbug about improvisation!' he used to declare. 'It makes you put your cards on the table, and what you haven't got you cannot show! If there's nothing there, you make a fool of yourself and everyone laughs at you! Is it not cowardly to shelter behind scores and counterpoint and act as if all that mattered were to avoid writing parallel fifths and to keep nicely to the rules?! Is it not cruel to lace the heart into a bodice that's so tight as to prevent it from breathing?'

'Come, come,' I chided. 'You yourself have improvised fugues and double fugues for us often enough, and the bodice of counterpoint seems to constrict *you* less than anyone!'

'That's just what I mean,' he retorted. 'The reason why *I* am not troubled by it is that I let my heart speak, even if I do adhere to the framework of the fugue! I prevail over that frame-work and make my listeners oblivious to it. . . .'

Later on, when he was devoting less time to improvisation and more to composing, many a colleague would try to taunt him with the memory of his earlier radical views and accuse him of lacking in principle.

Such reproaches upset him terribly—and with every good reason. He did not change his views for amusement or or gain: he acted from a better understanding born of experience.

[15]

SOME of this experience was extremely bitter. Beethoven did not everywhere encounter the love and friendship he found in the home of Prince Lichnowski. Because he failed to realise just how great at times were his demands on the indulgence and patience of his admirers, there were inevitably violent clashes here and there. Yet every time such a clash occurred, Beethoven was deeply hurt. He did not grasp what people resented in him: surely he was always upright and frank? As long as he lived he could never learn that more often than not frankness not only offends against good manners but also tends to infuriate other people. He certainly made many an enemy in the course of his life—but never for any other cause than his own excessive, childlike, incorrigible honesty. I call it incorrigible in the sense that he repeatedly made the error of expecting everyone he met to have that same goodness of heart which was so characteristic of himself. Naturally this put him hopelessly at the mercy of any opponent who handled him with a little guile, and throughout his life he was the easiest of men to dupe. But the pain he suffered when his own childlike honesty was misunderstood, and his disappointment at the lack of it in others, were both very deep and they did much to develop that embarrassing and often quite fierce mistrust which, as time went on, tended more and more to determine his attitude to life and, in his last years, to make him downright unsociable.

In the middle 'nineties—it must have been 1795 or '96—Beethoven paid his first visit to Prince Esterhazy at Eisenstadt. It was probably Haydn who had arranged the invitation; or it may even have been the young Prince Lobkowitz, in whose home, to Lichnowski's great chagrin, Beethoven had become a frequent and honoured guest. Esterhazy was known to be a zealous patron of all good music, and his anxiety to meet such a celebrated prodigy as Beethoven in his own home is understandable. On the other hand, the strictest etiquette prevailed at his court, and someone seemed to have made him uneasy about Beethoven's social imperfections and wayward temperament, for before the latter had received the official invitation from Esterhazy's chamberlain, I was visited, at the Hungarian Court Chancery, by a certain Gelinek who had only recently taken over the office of court chaplain in Eisenstadt. I knew this man from earlier days. He was a Czech by origin, and as he played the piano extremely well and was a man of wide culture, one often came across him in Viennese society. The priest's visit somewhat surprised me all the same, as we had never been on particularly good terms and were both well aware of our mutual antipathy.

Gelinek refrained from any allusion to our own relationship and came straight to the point. He had come on behalf of his Prince to ask me to visit Eisenstadt at the same time as the musician, Herr van Beethoven, with a view to my unobtrusively acting as the latter's guide and mentor for the duration of his stay at the Esterhazy court. The Prince had heard that Herr van Beethoven enjoyed my friendship, and as Herr van Beethoven was notorious for being none too well versed in court etiquette and would thus be in danger—quite unintentionally of course—of committing some breach or other, the Prince was desirous of easing his somewhat delicate position—obviously without Herr van Beethoven's being in any way aware of it. It was hardly necessary to add that the Prince was counting on my discretion.

I found Gelinek's communication distasteful, for it seemed likely that he himself had strengthened the Prince's misgivings regarding Beethoven's presentability. Besides, I felt the correct solution should have been respectfully to suggest to His Serene Highness that it would be better in the circumstances to forego Beethoven's company altogether. However, two considerations deterred me from giving Esterhazy's emissary a negative reply. The first was out of regard for Beethoven himself. I had no right to bar his way to the Court of Eisenstadt. It was too important for his reputation and future career that he should go there. And if his first appearance in Eisenstadt were to have unpleasant associations for me personally, it was clearly my duty as a friend not to evade them. Secondly, Count Palffy, my chief and patron, was a close friend of Prince Esterhazy; this fact made it impossible for me to refuse to fulfil a wish which the latter had put to me as a personal request. Consequently I accepted Gelinek's proposal and asked him to convey my most humble thanks to the Prince for the trust he had shown me.

A few weeks later I was seated next to Beethoven in one of the Esterhazy carriages, and enjoyable though this journey to Eisenstadt proved to be, it became obvious at the moment of our arrival that the stay was not to be a particularly happy one.

We were received by an elderly footman whose duty was to conduct us to our rooms. Having reached the first floor of the west wing and opened a door, he turned to me and said:

'Your Grace's apartment.'

'And where is Herr van Beethoven's?'

At this the man became embarrassed and, with a look of helplessness, asked in Hungarian:

'Might I ask your Grace . . . on behalf of his Excellency the Court Chamberlain . . .'

'Speak German!' I interrupted. 'Herr van Beethoven doesn't understand Hungarian.'

The flunkey swallowed hard, squared his shoulders and recited his piece:

'His Excellency is not clear whether Herr van Beethoven is of noble birth or not. If the first case applies, I am instructed to accommodate Herr van Beethoven in the apartment next door; if not I must ask Herr van Beethoven kindly to follow me to the third floor.'

Seeing an angry flush rise in Beethoven's cheeks, I hastened to forestall him.

'Open that other door immediately!' I ordered the footman. 'Tell his Excellency those were my instructions.'

Visibly relieved, the old man did as he was told and withdrew in silence.

I led Beethoven into the room that had been opened for him and made sure that it was as good as my own. He cast an appraising glance around him, waited for the younger flunkey who had carried up our luggage to close the doors behind him, and said, with a quiet composure that I found far more ominous than the outburst I had expected:

'I should like to return home immediately.'

For the moment I made no reply, waiting to see what would follow. But he had nothing more to say and fixed a challenging gaze upon me as he in turn awaited my answer.

'I understand your wish perfectly. But I would beg you to consider the matter thoroughly before taking such a drastic step.'

I spoke with the utmost evenness and calm.

'Why?' he demanded.

'Because your departure would be a grave insult to the Prince. He personally had no intention of offending you.'

'An artist of my class is worth a hundred noblemen.'

'I, for one, do not need reminding of that,' I rejoined. 'And the Prince probably thinks the same. What has just happened is merely a question of court routine. The Chamberlain must observe the rules of his office. I think you should dismiss such a minor incident from your mind.'

Beethoven did not reply and went to the window, where, hands clasped behind him he stood staring down at the castle courtyard. I felt it best to hold my peace while he made up his mind. At length he turned round to me again:

'Perhaps you're right,' he said, and set about unpacking his valise. But his good mood had gone.

Nor did it return as long as we were at Eisenstadt. Indeed, the atmosphere of the Esterhazy court was hardly calculated to have an encouraging or relaxing effect on a man of Beethoven's type. In those days there was even more ritual and formality at Eisenstadt than at the Imperial Court in Vienna. Throughout our three-day visit Beethoven was reserved and taciturn—sometimes almost uncivil. He played on several occasions—neither particularly well nor particularly badly. One could tell that his heart was not in it.

The Prince was undoubtedly disappointed in him, having expected something better than this. But he gave no outward sign and treated Beethoven with special consideration. One lady of the court had the misfortune to ask Beethoven whether he knew Mozart's operas. He pulled an indescribably rude face and casually replied:

'No—and I don't want to, either. I might lose my originality if I did. . . .'

When we were at last in the carriage again, with Eisenstadt some miles behind us, something like a deep sigh escaped from Beethoven's breast:

'I cannot understand how Haydn endured it there for so long. . . .'

'He didn't in the long run.' I smiled. 'And you mustn't forget that it wasn't the present Prince whom Haydn liked so much. It was his father.'

'Was he any different?'

'Evidently he was. More after the style of Maria Theresa, I imagine. The times and the people were different then. People were more vital, more natural—more simple, even. Despite all the constraint and ceremony.'

'Kaiser Josef!' said Beethoven after a short pause. 'Kaiser Josef—that was the man for me!'

'Did you know him, then?'

'I was presented to him once. He was very kind to me—something for which I shall always remember him. But that isn't what I'm thinking of. I mean everything about him. He had a real heart. He accepted a man for what he was worth. And he hated priestcraft.'

All of a sudden he giggled to himself.

'That Gelinek!' he said. 'I taught him a proper lesson!'

'Gelinek?' I asked in surprise. 'But I thought I saw you having several friendly talks together?'

'You did, in the main hall—and we were talking about music. But on Sunday, just before luncheon, he came up to my room. . . .'

'And what did he want?'

'He asked me,' said Beethoven in great amusement, 'why I hadn't been to Mass. . . .'

'And what did you tell him?'

'Oh, I told him to mind his own business. I said I wasn't one of his flock, as far as I knew.'

'Good God!'

'You haven't heard the worst of it yet,' said Beethoven, serious again now. 'He wouldn't be put off and began to appeal to my conscience.'

'What then?'

'That was when I turned on him. I told him I understood much more about God than he did, for all his theology. I didn't need any help from the likes of him to be on good terms with God. God couldn't be caught with golden monstrances, I said, nor summoned by tinkling bells on Sunday mornings between nine and ten.—He stared at me with those big, cowlike eyes and then threw up his hands and shouted: "You're a Protestant!" I shouted back that he was a fool, and that I was no more a Protestant than he was. But, I told him, I was at least a man—a free man, not a toady. Which was more than he could claim to be. . . .'

'And what happened then?'

Beethoven started giggling to himself again. 'He'd had enough. He said he would pray for me. Then he went.'

For a while I was silent. At length I asked very cautiously:

'Do you realise *where* he went?'

'Why, where do you think he was going?' asked Beethoven, much astonished.

'To the Prince, of course,' I replied.

'Why should he? What had that to do with the Prince?'

'*Ach*, my dear Beethoven!' I cried. 'Will you never become a little more worldly-minded? Don't you see that Gelinek is jealous of you? *He* plays the piano, too, remember, and has a tremendous opinion of his own playing. And don't you understand that the Prince is very Catholic and that Gelinek need only give him the merest hint of what you flung at him on Sunday for the Prince never to invite you there again?'

'I thought the Prince invited me to hear my music, not to send me scuttling off to Mass.—Do I play any worse for not going to Church?'

'Of course not,' I cried in some impatience. 'But unfortunately you play much too well for an envious man not to seize every chance to harm you.'

'Shame on him!' said Beethoven. 'And a priest, too!'

'Since you can't abide clerics, why should you blame Gelinek for behaving like one?'

That seemed to have touched him on the raw at last. He pressed his lips together, as he always did in moments of stress, and for a long time said nothing.

'The higher you climb, my dear Beethoven,' I began once more, laying my hand on his, 'the higher you climb, the more famous you become, and the more clearly people realise that you are what God appointed you to be—the deeper you should learn to mistrust everyone till he has proved his intentions towards you are honest.'

Then he let himself go, and I had the feeling that he was at long last venting all the rancour and bitterness that had accumulated in his heart at Eisenstadt.

'But that's terrible! To mistrust everyone until he proves

that he doesn't deserve it? It's inhuman—it's the negation of all goodness, decency and morality! How can you ask such a thing of me? If what you say were true, I simply wouldn't want to live any longer! There would be no sense in making music any more! How can a man make music for people who wish him ill?! Music would no longer have any purpose: it would be a lie, a blasphemy! No, no, I will never follow you along that road! I know you mean well. But never *that*—never, as long as I live! If you are going to deprive me of my faith in humanity and make me believe that men are mean and low and incapable of sublime inspiration, if you insist that the human being is not *good*, then our ways must part—then I no longer believe in your friendship—I no longer *want* your friendship!!'

He had snatched his hand away and furiously turned his back on me, pounding with both fists against the upholstery of the carriage. Once again he shrieked 'No—no—never!' and then: 'Tell him to stop! I want to get out! I want to be alone!'

'Do be sensible, Beethoven!' I retorted sharply, 'and stop acting like a child! I never said anything of the kind!—There's not the least reason why a man should become misanthropic just because certain individuals he meets do not—or will not, or cannot—understand him! I'm merely warning you to be more careful! And my only motive in doing so is that I hate to see your own excessive magnanimity and trust being abused by others! I am not saying you should alter! All I say is that you shouldn't hand out your generosity and trust so indiscriminately! The fact that you give people your music is really quite enough! With the other things you should learn to be a little more sparing. That's all the advice I wanted to give you—as a loyal friend. And now do please calm yourself. It really isn't as bad as all that. . . .'

The storm in his heart seemed to be abating. Though he kept his back towards me and continued to stare out of the window in silence for some time afterwards, I sensed that he was calming down. I suppose we had gone another mile before he finally turned round again.

'You mean that I should learn . . . *only* to make music? To let what you call my magnanimity and trust speak only through my music? It that what you mean?'

He said it very softly, rather like a man talking to himself.

'Now you're going to the other extreme,' I replied. 'Let us say that it would be much better if people like Gelinek saw nothing of your magnanimity and trust beyond what your music cares to tell. . . .'

Once again he brooded for a while before replying. When he spoke it was clear that he wished to bring the matter to a close.

'It may be that you are right,' he said. 'I must think it over again. But after all, what concern of *mine* is the meanness of other people . . . ?'

[16]

SOON after Beethoven's visit to Eisenstadt it became known that he was thinking of leaving Vienna. Guests from other cities and other lands who had met him in the Viennese salons had taken stories of his genius home with them, and it was hardly surprising that offers should reach him from the outside world.

I clearly remember a discussion—parts of which were most heated—held in this connection by a number of Beethoven's most prominent patrons. They had asked me to attend in the hope of persuading me to talk Beethoven out of his project. Lichnowski was the one most strongly opposed to losing Beethoven, and it cannot be denied that he had good reason for being out of humour.

By this time the Archbishopric of Cologne had virtually disappeared from the map of Europe. The Archduke Max had lost his throne and had little prospect of regaining it in the foreseeable future. Beethoven's subsidies from Bonn had long ceased—'and,' said Lichnowski, 'he's indebted to us for having been able to find a firm footing here in Vienna. We've put him in the way of a livelihood that's infinitely more agreeable and satisfying than anything he knew previously. We've paid him handsome fees, and his pupils are all recruited from our own circles. In short, where would he be without us? I really don't think it would be fair of him to turn his back on us now and seek for fortune elsewhere. . . .'

'My dear Karl,' Lobkowitz interrupted, 'we all understand what you mean and we know, too, that your wife and yourself have the strongest claim on his gratitude. . . . But is it really so certain that Beethoven's going to turn his back on us for good? To me, at least, he has only spoken of doing an extensive guest tour. He left me with the impression that he intended to come back here. . . .'

'Oh, yes, that's what *he* says,' Lichnowski retorted. 'On the other hand, I'm informed that considerable progress has been made in certain negotiations to tie him to Berlin for good.'

'Do you believe he would feel happier in Berlin than with us? At a court ruled by mistresses and full of intrigues and backstairs liaisons?' asked Lobkowitz, still following his train of thought. 'Let him go by all means: he's sure to return. And if he's successful out there, the ultimate credit will be ours. . . . What do you think Zmeskall?'

'I feel we should not try to restrain him,' I said. 'If only because his contrariness and mistrust, which are both very strong, would be provoked by any counteraction on our part—however well-meaning—and would only make him more determined than ever. And his plans are by no means based on material considerations alone—that is, on considerations which we outsiders can appreciate or judge. I, for one, am convinced that he's going through some kind of inner crisis—that there are things going on inside him which he does not fully understand and which are unsettling and tormenting him. To my mind his plans are at least partly due to a desire—possibly a quite unconscious one—to seek external distraction from these obscure inner problems of his. . . .'

'What *are* you talking about?' asked Lichnowski. 'What sort of inner crises and problems are these supposed to be? Please don't be offended, *lieber Freund*, but you know I am none too charitable in matters of this kind. Artists have their moods: no one knows that better than I. And you all know that I will overlook very many moods in a great artist—none more than in Beethoven. But I will not have the kind of mental confusion and slovenliness which seems bound to go hand in hand with a great artistic genius explained away by obscure arguments. Perhaps I've been far too indulgent in many things already. . . .'

I cannot say that Lichnowski's refusal to accept my view very much surprised me, and I made no further attempt to make my meaning clear.

'I don't know that friend Zmeskall is so very wrong,' said Lobkowitz when he saw that I did not intend to reply. 'I've often wondered whether we don't take such things a little too lightly. But we'll leave that—it might lead us too far. In any case, I agree that our opposition may only aggravate the situation. Beethoven would think we wished to impede him in something which will be to his advantage and gain. I'm in favour of letting him go on his tour—he'll come back in good time. He has settled down very comfortably with us—only when he's gone will he realise *how* comfortably. . . .'

Lichnowski, however, was not to be so easily appeased. He had a great deal more to say and the debate showed no sign of ending. But when, with growing insistence, he urged me to 'bring Beethoven to reason' and make him see how unfair and ungrateful his behaviour was, I had no choice but to give a blunt refusal.

'And why do you refuse?' asked Lichnowski rather irritably.

'Because I am resolved—if possible—to retain Beethoven's friendship,' I told him. 'Because I don't want to do anything that might hurt him.'

'Even when he behaves so outrageously?' Lichnowski cried.

'I don't think he deserves such a reproach. His standards are not the same as ours. I have respect for his standards. . . .'

'More than you have for ours, in other words?'

'I didn't say that,' I replied quietly. 'I mean simply this: if we are satisfied with his music, we should try to do justice to the man behind it.'

Lichnowski stared at me in exasperation and then, with a shrug of his shoulders, turned away.

In due course Beethoven set out on his travels, full of ambitious plans.

'How long do you expect to be away?' I asked when he came to take leave of me.

'What a foolish question!' he laughed. 'As long as it suits me. . . .'

[17]

The reports we had of Beethoven during his absence were most conflicting. There were, of course, most enthusiastic accounts of his artistic accomplishment, his fascinating skill and the power of his musical personality;

but at the same time we learnt that he had, unfortunately, not the least idea how to make himself pleasant to other people. On a number of occasions, in Prague and later in Berlin, he managed to offend influential personages without whose goodwill he had no prospect whatever of establishing any lasting connections. It seemed to be generally agreed that he was far too cross-grained, self-willed and unpolished for one to find any pleasure in his company.

We were not surprised to see him back in Vienna before six months were out, and his principal patrons—with Lichnowski and Lobkowitz well to the fore—made no small parade of the fact that Vienna was apparently the only place with the right approach to a genius of Beethoven's rank.

I, for my part, preferred to believe that the journey to Prague and Berlin had brought the young musician closer to certain perceptions which had been maturing within him for some time past. After all, it frequently happens that external experiences and the impressions of a new environment can teach a man things about himself whose novelty is only apparent.

Be that as it may, Beethoven returned from his tour a very changed man. He had lost much of his impetuous good nature and become more reserved. It seemed as though his experiences had taught him to be more retiring and to afford those around him less share in what went on within him.

The most striking and—to my mind—significant development was that he returned to Vienna with a new attitude towards his professional activity—almost as if he had found a new *genre*. Where he had previously been quite ready to perform in a social setting and to assume rather the air of an ordinary guest in the music-lovers' salons which he frequented, it now became plain that he drew a clear distinction between himself and his listeners, that he no longer wished to merge in the company around him, that he preferred to be one apart who made society, as it were, a gift of his art—a voluntary gift that he was at liberty to withdraw whenever he pleased. In the same connection he ceased to confine his activities to the homes of his patrons and began to feel his way to the public at large and the anonymity of the concert hall. At the same time he began to associate more and more with his musical confrères—often in almost offensive disregard of those members of the aristocracy who had hitherto considered him their more or less exclusive possession.

In the weeks immediately following his return to Vienna he treated me with cautious reserve, and only when he saw that I had not the remotest intention of criticising his new course and even less of interfering in his personal affairs, only when he realised that I conceded him every right as a man to do or leave undone and to think and feel whatever he thought fit, did he begin to seek my company again and treat me with the same freedom and familiarity as before.

Indeed, there was a period of some months in which he showed great eagerness for my society and repeatedly prevailed on me to spend long evenings with him in taverns and hostelries—all from an urge to unburden himself and put into words whatever happened to be on his mind. It was not always easy to fulfil the rôle he thus allotted me. For often enough those hours in the taverns proved trivial and unproductive and passed away in disjointed daydreams, crude jokes and coarse chatter which severely taxed my patience. But I sensed that he needed me and that I must not fail him. Though he did not drink excessively on these evenings, he drank quite a lot, and often enough it depended on the odd glass of wine whether he would launch into the most serious discussions or lose himself in sheer banalities.

[18]

TODAY, of course, I can no longer single out a particular evening when he imparted anything of unusual interest or significance. I can at most hope to bring out the quintessence of what he had to say by fitting together fragments of numerous different conversations.

In the last analysis everything he said amounted to this. He was gradually becoming aware that he could no longer make do with improvisation alone, that he could no longer contend with a creative will whose only outlet was through his own performances at the keyboard. He found that he was missing both the object and the essence of his real mission in life.

It was clear that his ultimate purpose had been badly retarded by the fact that his audiences in the past had been limited to the courts and high society. He roundly cursed the salons that were so proud of their class distinction and superior knowledge; he ranted about the people whose aim was not to capture the true worth of his music but to pander to their own vanity; most of all he reviled those ladies of all ages whose sole object was to glorify *him* and for whom his mastery was merely an excuse for importunate advances. He inveighed with particular violence against the corruption of the Berlin Court, the spinelessness of the King of Prussia and the intrigues of the kept women who were the real power behind the throne.

'What have I come to,' he once cried, thumping his fist on the table, 'when the verdict passed on my music by a whole court, a whole city, is dependent on the whim of a royal whore?'

Then, one day, he began to ponder how he should set about bringing his playing to the people, to the broad masses of simple, unspoilt, upright men and women. 'If I go into the concert halls,' he shouted, 'whom do I find there? The same stupid idiots and cackling geese who sit around gaping at me in the drawing-rooms. And before I get there I must scuttle from one house to the next humbly begging for subscriptions!—Oh, it's all quite wrong, ridiculously wrong! If I had my way, I'd have my piano planted in the middle of the Stephansplatz and play under the open sky one fine Sunday afternoon. Then perhaps my music would get where it belongs—to real men and women, not dressed-up dolls and lounge lizards. . . .'

Once he had worked himself up like this it was useless to point out, however tactfully, that he was being rather unjust and that such sweeping generalisations must inevitably include many an admirer of his who was deeply and seriously affected by his music. He was furious, and had to give vent to his fury somehow.

But this was only one side of his inner torment and strife. It was obvious that he was now beginning—entirely with regard to himself and irrespective of his public—to have doubts about the purpose and course of his career to date.

'I'm not the same every day of the week,' he said, 'either in what I feel or in what my feelings try to express. I might be ill, in the wrong mood or unable to give of my best—and that could be just when I had my finest audience before me. Then they would go home disappointed. . . .'

Apart from this, he began to realise that much of what he had to give might not yet be intelligible to the audiences of the day. What was to become of his music when its strains had died away, never to return? For that matter, why *should* they die away for ever? Was it not a thousand pities that they did?

Very well, then—what if he did decide to commit to a music score all the things that went straight into his fingers in moments of inspired improvisation? That was when he would face all the dangers such a process entailed: loss of freshness and originality; laborious effort in the place of spontaneous expression. On the other hand, his media would be greatly extended—there would be singing, chamber-music and orchestra. But that, again, would mean entrusting the execution to other musicians who couldn't possibly capture what he had felt when he wrote it down. . . .

'You're surely musical enough,' he cried, 'to understand that our method of scoring is quite useless? That it can't possibly record what one really feels and is seeking to express? Oh, it's enough to drive a man to despair—to be filled to the brim with visions and then to have to sit down in front of five lines, a grill of five eternally parallel lines, and to fill in all those heads and tails and pennants!

'The rules are what drive me mad! All this talk about counterpoint and how to do things the "right" way! If all the counterpoint experts in the world have invented nothing better to bring out the beauty and truth of my visions than a strait-jacket of rules and restrictions about what you "must" do and what you "mustn't" do—then they're all bunglers and botchers and have no more idea of what I call music than a bull has of dancing a minuet!'

[19]

I KNOW that I am taking a bold step and that many people will think it far-fetched and high-flown if I now try to sum up and explain the true meaning of what was going on in Beethoven at that time—but I have not lived to be seventy to be shy about my opinions.

Beethoven had long known—deep down inside him and before the ultimate tribunal of his own conscience as an artist—that he was on the wrong tack with his improvisation and that by this alone he could never do justice to his real mission. He knew that his vocation was to compose, to create finely-executed works of music that would be products of his own genius and yet ultimately have their own independent existence. He knew this—and was afraid. He was afraid of failing, afraid of not being able to master the profusion, beauty and power of his visions when he came to give them musical shape. It is this fear which explains the confused and tormented state of his mind at that time.

Yes, I know—people will tell me how ridiculous it is to suggest that the very man who wrote those symphonies, quartets, sonatas and overtures should have been afraid of not achieving what in fact he did achieve. . . . But I say that by very reason of the unprecedented novelty, depth and power of his later works he *must* have been terribly afraid before he finally attained the mastery which made him capable of such creations. At the time of which I am speaking he was becoming more and more sensible of what was within him and striving to reach the light; he was filled to bursting point with glorious, mighty sound-visions; but he was as yet unable to take them in his grasp because he still lacked the technical means to do so. The task of acquiring these means still lay ahead of him, and I, for one, find nothing surprising in his having been intimidated by the prospect.

Many a person in the same position would have given in to his fear and shunned such a task. How easy it was to shun! Personal and material success lay so completely on the side of the shunner. As a pianist and improvisator he had no competition to fear: he was the king of this realm. But, like a Hercules at the parting of the ways, he chose hard effort and sacrifice.

In the course of those long, trying and often terrifying evenings at the tables of Viennese taverns and in the company often of drunken cabmen and labourers, I gained a profound insight into something which is today clear to anyone with ears on his head—the sternness of the moral duty with which Beethoven considered his genius had confronted him.

[20]

But the same thing happened to Beethoven as would have happened to any healthy-minded man in a similar position. He came to realise that no amount of talking would help him and that there was only one way of solving such problems—by hard, dogged work.

And the end to his doubts, the fruit of his labours—how laughable it sounds in retrospect!—was his attainment of his own style, his awakening to that creative power which is for all time stamped with the name of Beethoven.

Every connoisseur of his work is aware that this awakening of the real, authentic Beethoven is to be found in the Third Symphony, the so-called Eroica. This is the work that marks the end of all that has gone before; it is the first to show Beethoven in full possession of his inimitable mastery.

All previous compositions are mere milestones along the toilsome road that led to the consummate skill of the Eroica. And in case there is anyone who does not instinctively feel the truth of this, let me add that I have Beethoven's own word for it.

[21]

On the road that led to the Eroica, however, there were many other things, too—things of the utmost significance. Before I speak of these, I would beg leave briefly to review certain technical aspects of Beethoven's previous compositions.

I do not believe that anyone who takes the trouble in later years to investigate the inner continuity of Beethoven's life work can possibly overlook one most important fact about the creative period preceding the Eroica: namely, that in those years of preparation and tireless struggle for mastery, two quite separate lines of development ran side by side. On one hand Beethoven was clearly striving to attain the ideal of consummate musical beauty; on the other he sought the ideal of cogent musical expression. The first line finds fulfilment in the six String Quartets, Opus 18, and the Septet, Opus 20, the other in the piano sonatas in C sharp minor, Opus 27, and D minor, Opus 31.

The most striking characteristic of the inimitable personal style which Beethoven first achieved in the Eroica is, in my humble opinion, to be found in the hitherto unknown balance between musical beauty and human truth and worth—in the fact that a human declaration of particular depth and validity found expression in a music of unrivalled perfection. For anyone who can grasp this it is most edifying to see how, in those years before the Eroica, the master-to-be, the still groping artist, stalked his vague ideal along separate paths, equipping himself as he went with an assured technical skill and a power of musical expression, both of which, in the fullness of time, he was to unify in one and the same masterpiece—the Eroica.

As I see it, there lies in the methodical continuity of this development, in the harmony and unity of its outcome, a wisdom so wonderful that it can never be surpassed. . . . And with that I shall leave it. I am not one to make a great song about such things.

[22]

AND now I shall try to speak of those other things which, side by side with Beethoven's development as an artist in the period preceding the Eroica, also exerted a profound and decisive influence.

[23]

EVERY friend of Beethoven knows that the Eroica has not always borne this name, that until the summer of 1804—to be precise, until the day on which it became known in Vienna that Napoleon was proclaiming himself Emperor of France—the word 'Bonaparte' stood on the title page. Indeed, there is a quite vital connection between the impact of the Corsican on Beethoven and the latter's first major symphonic work, and to put this in its proper perspective I must go back a little in my narrative.

I have already indicated that Beethoven struck many of those who came in contact with him as a 'revolutionary', as an adherent of those ideas which found their first practical application in the great French popular movement of 1789. I have also indicated, though, that his politico-social ideals must have deviated very soon afterwards from the forms and substance of the French Revolution in its later stages; for anyone who thought the Emperor Josef an admirable sovereign obviously could not condone regicide and mass execution.

I have met revolutionaries of every hue in my lifetime, and my observation has always been that the particular philosophy or course of action they advocated invariably had its origins in some galling experience of a very personal kind. If, for example, one of them had had to suffer under the despotism of a particularly worthless potentate, he was usually in favour of consigning all crowned heads to the guillotine. If another had lost a protracted and important lawsuit, nothing was dearer to his heart than to revolutionise the legislation or the judiciary. And so on. All this is perfectly natural and human. Were it not so, the utopian definitions of revolutionary principle would have little prospect of luring the dog away from his warm place by the stove.

The personal humiliations whose sources young Beethoven

would like to have seen removed by the revolutionary upheavals of the century then drawing to its close were by no means very bitter. They may rather be said to have originated in one notably susceptible facet of his own make-up: he was by nature an extremely proud man and had an unshakable belief in the importance and dignity of the individual human being striving for high moral and spiritual aims.

The circumstances into which he was born were far from unpleasant for a man of his background. Indeed, the social conditions of the day in the Electorate of Cologne were, relatively speaking, most favourable.

This little corner of the Empire was far removed from all political and military conflict; the trades and crafts had benefited from decades of continuous peace; the people as a whole were passably prosperous and found no serious obstacles to their enjoyment of life. As for the Archduke Max himself, he had many qualities for which young Beethoven could feel nothing but whole-hearted sympathy: he was entirely dedicated to the ideals of Emperor Josef II of Hapsburg-Lorraine, and under his rule the city of Bonn had acquired not only its own university but even a German national theatre fostering serious and genuine art. Apart from this, young Beethoven's official and personal contacts with his ruler had served only to convince him of the latter's understanding and benevolent nature. All these things went to make up an environment hardly likely to result in Beethoven's growing up a revolutionary terrorist or even a radical. What vexed him in the conditions he found around him, what struck him as crying out for reform, were all things which needed neither a guillotine nor a reign of bloody terror to eliminate.

What he found quite intolerable was, to begin with, the antiquated ceremonial with which he had to contend as a young citizen of the Archbishopric of Cologne. It hurt his pride and sense of dignity whenever he was compelled, in both spoken and written communication with his ruler and the latter's authorities, to employ a servile and humble form of speech; it irked him to have to adopt a cringing, almost fawning attitude towards members of the Court and the local aristocracy, particularly when he had become old enough to realise that the privileged status of such personages was only too often in blatant contrast to their real value as human beings. It was thus inevitable that he should become entirely pre-occupied with the problem of finding more suitable standards for the rules which governed men's social and official relations with each other.

Beethoven's views on reform were concerned with how to win absolute individual freedom in the intellectual and, above all, religious spheres. This was the reason why he so approved of Emperor Josef's anti-clericalism. Though I have no personal experience of the conditions in Bonn during Beethoven's youth, I find no difficulty in forming what is probably an accurate mental picture of the all-pervading, priest-ridden influences of the era. The good prelates can hardly have been less obese, selfish, sycophantic, scheming and libidinous in Bonn than in any other ecclesiastic principality. In Beethoven's case there was the additional fact that from earliest childhood he had had a strongly developed religious sense—though he became increasingly aware as time went on that this sense was utterly incompatible with Catholic doctrine. But more of that later.

To cut a long story short, Beethoven's 'revolutionary' views and aspirations derived entirely from a deep-rooted conviction of man's intrinsic worth and from an ardent longing to see the world organised in such a way that there was nothing to hinder the free development of that worth.

He was deeply disappointed by the chaos into which the French Revolution had slid and by the growing influence of the mob. It greatly pained him to see a movement which had originally seemed inspired by the most idealistic motives threatening to go down in a sea of blood and horror. One can readily understand, therefore, the enthusiasm with which he welcomed the advent of that young general who in the nick of time used his fascinating and gifted personality to snatch the Revolution back from the abyss of terror and restored its spiritual merits to the realm of law and order. For Beethoven Napoleon became the personification of his humanitarian ideals, a hero of freedom, the God-sent creator of a civilisation which guaranteed all well-disposed Europeans room in which to live and breathe. So much has happened in the last five and thirty years that it is perhaps just as well to point out how greatly young Beethoven's view of Bonaparte's mission accorded with that of the majority of European youth. One easily forgets today that in those times no one could possibly guess what the Corsican would one day perpetrate in the name of the French Revolution.

The Peace of Campoformio of 1797, besides laying down those territorial modifications so drastic for the Austrian monarchy, also provided that normal diplomatic relations must be maintained between the French Republic and our Emperor. I say 'must' because, for all people amicably disposed towards the House of Hapsburg, this was one of the bitterest consequences of the lost campaign. It meant having to offer one's hand to, and enter into social relations with, the official representative of a government with the blood of Marie Antoinette on its hands. . . . The Emperor himself went so far in his resistance to this affront to his principles that a fresh crisis very nearly ensued: for several months running he refused, every time with a different excuse, to receive Napoleon's envoy for the presentation of his credentials. For France's first envoy to Vienna this entailed leading a life of complete isolation for many weeks after his arrival in our capital. It was against court etiquette for any member of Viennese court society to enter into relations with him before he had been received by the Emperor, and it is hardly necessary to add that everyone close to the Court showed malicious delight at the envoy's social quarantine and took good care to do nothing to alleviate this hated man's position.

The envoy who was given such an unfriendly reception at his new post was General Bernadotte, afterwards Marshal of France, Duke of Pontecorvo and finally—exactly twenty years later—King of Sweden. He was a man of wit and intelligence and countered this social ostracism by creating with due emphasis on the republican character of his office—a busy centre of social activity within his own four walls. His retinue included a whole team of French artists and scholars who forthwith got in touch with their local counterparts. As a result Vienna lived to see many bourgeois intellectuals—scientists, poets, writers, musicians and exponents of the fine arts—eagerly accepting Bernadotte's invitations, all the more so when he turned out to be a man of great culture with whom one could converse freely and intelligently on any subject.

Beethoven was one of the first people to be drawn into Bernadotte's circle. He might almost be said to have flown into his arms. Here at last was his long desired opportunity to enter the world of his idolised revolutionary genius; here at last he could find personal contact with a representative of the liberal, humanitarian ideals which so inspired him. The fact that he was able at the same time to demonstrate publicly against the Austrian Emperor and his reactionary policies was probably an added source of gratification to him. He was simply a reformer in the spirit of Josef II, and that was that. It is a certain fact that his conduct was viewed with great disfavour at the highest level and that the Emperor never forgave him.

Beethoven was a regular guest in the French envoy's house and obviously felt very much at home there. Bernadotte, who had too sound a grasp of music and human nature to underestimate Beethoven's importance for one moment, did all he could to bring him under his sway: he treated him with every possible distinction and, of course, gave appropriate instructions to his retinue. Of the musicians he had brought from France the most important was Rudolf Kreutzer, who later won world renown as a violinist and to whom Beethoven dedicated the great and extremely intricate violin sonata of that name.

There cannot, to my mind, be the least doubt that Beethoven not only made music at Bernadotte's house but also talked a great deal of politics into the bargain. It is true that during the few months of the first French envoy's sojourn in Vienna he more or less deliberately abandoned those of us whose convictions or official positions made us join in the ostracism of Bernadotte, thus putting us out of touch with him for a time, but later on, after Bernadotte had gone, it did strike me how much Beethoven had absorbed of the early-Napoleonic ideology on culture and State. I confess that at the time I thoroughly envied him his intimate connection with that household, for I, too, would have been glad to gain first-hand knowledge of an intellectual world which could not fail to catch the imagination of every progressive-minded young man.

It is, at all events, quite certain—Beethoven himself having confirmed the fact to me at a later date—that Bernadotte prevailed on him to give artistic expression to his conception of Napoleonic genius through the medium of a great symphonic work interpreting and glorifying the revolutionary ideal which Napoleon personified. It is also quite certain that Beethoven enthusiastically seized on this suggestion of Bernadotte's—which testifies, incidentally, to the latter's great political acumen—and immediately set about tackling the considerable musical problems involved.

Shortly afterwards—in April '98—there occurred those disturbing incidents which led to Bernadotte's recall from Vienna.

After the Emperor had finally been compelled to receive

the envoy of the French Republic and the latter had been able to take up his proper official and social position, it became increasingly apparent that the tensions and differences between Bernadotte and the antagonists of all that he stood for were far too great ever to be settled peaceably. The mutual irritations and deliberate annoyances increased alarmingly, and in due course, on the occasion of some holiday or other in the French Republic, Bernadotte felt called upon—and formally he was quite within his rights in doing so—to hoist the Tricolour on his residence. This, in view of the prevailing mood, was an intolerable provacation.

Mobs banded together with the connivance of the police. There were riots in front of the French Embassy, patriotic songs were sung, and stones began to fly. Only when it was clear that the building was about to be stormed did the police intervene and with great difficulty prevent the worst from happening till a company of troops arrived at the double to restore order. I hardly need describe the diplomatic interlude that followed. It is enough to say that Bernadotte could no longer be tolerated in Vienna and that the Paris Directorate had to accede to his official recall even after he had actually left, the Imperial Government having refused to accept responsibility for his personal safety.

After all this trouble I looked forward with some curiosity to seeing Beethoven again. We met quite by chance in an inn, and it seemed he disapproved of Bernadotte's conduct.

'It serves him right,' he averred. 'What right had he to dangle his three-coloured duster in front of our noses. . . .'

I made no reply, and he must have seen from my face that, far from being surprised, I was actually rather amused by this unexpected *volte-face*.

'Damnation!' he roared, 'take that silly smirk off your face! The Tricolour is *France*, not something to provoke us

Germans with! And you can see that even his own Government repudiates him! You can stake your life on it that Bonaparte will tell him a thing or two when he gets home! Bonaparte is much too great a man to condone foolishness of that kind! He has far too much respect for us Germans to want to make Frenchmen of us! Didn't you know that Goethe's *Werther* is his favourite reading?—Well, then . . .'

Growing calmer, he added with great gravity and emphasis:

'Bonaparte knows what freedom is. Bonaparte knows that the primary meaning of freedom is that everyone should be what God's will had made him. Bonaparte knows that the Tricolour belongs in Paris, not Vienna. *Ach*, none of you understand him! For the simple reason that you cannot *believe*. . . . But *I* shall show you one day what Bonaparte is and what he stands for. . . .'

It was then that he began to tell me of his great plan to write a symphony which would bring home to all of us the real truth about Bonaparte.

[24]

It is quite amazing, by the way, with what careless rapture legend encroaches on the lives of important men. Even in Beethoven's lifetime I more than once heard it said that Bernadotte had urged him to write a symphony immortalising Napoleon's campaign in Egypt—and that this was the very purport of the Eroica. In particular, it was claimed that the first movement depicted the crossing of the Mediterranean by the French expeditionary force and that the second, the famous funeral march, was an expression of grief at the disastrous naval engagement of Aboukir. Now it is obvious nonsense to suggest that Bernadotte could have made such a suggestion to Beethoven. He had left Vienna long before Napoleon began to move on Egypt or the news of this reached us. Besides, it is utterly wrong to identify the various movements of the Eroica with programme music. The Eroica is not a narrative interpretation of material events, it is . . . but before I express any views on the subject, I had better tell something of those other human experiences which play such an important rôle in the story behind the Eroica. A prelimary survey of these will make it far easier to give a convincing account of what the Eroica really is and implies.

At all events, the numerous and often unscrupulous legends which I have discovered about Beethoven's life and career contributed in no small measure to my resolve to record what I know and think of the musician. If such things can gain currency only three years after the great musician's death, what will it be like later on when there are none of his contemporaries left to refute them?

[25]

And now I have reached a point in my narrative which I have approached with growing apprehension. It is a point where tact and indiscretion lie so close together that even an old man like myself finds it hard to discern the fine dividing line.

I could, of course, confine myself to the bare statement that about this time—the exact date is immaterial—Beethoven seriously considered getting married. I would then have to explain that the lady of his choice was a well-known and successful singer—young, beautiful and unusually talented—and that the young musician's deep and passionate devotion to her was very understandable. Next, however, it would be my unpleasant duty to record that the lady rejected Beethoven's marriage proposal, doing so with a pitiless candour which can at most be excused by the fact that she and Beethoven had been professionally acquainted since their days together at the National Theatre of blessed memory in Bonn. She informed him quite bluntly that for one thing he was too ugly and for another too mad. Had I told the story thus, it would be only too easy to draw a cheap and effective contrast between the artistic importance Beethoven was later to manifest to the world and the disgraceful behaviour of the young woman who treated him with such heartless folly. And, seen from the outside, this would fully accord with the facts. These things really did occur, and Beethoven's mortification was undoubtedly deep and enduring.

Were I to go no further than that, however, I should be neglecting the heart of the matter—neglecting that inner truth which means so much to me and, I trust, to my readers.

It would be grossly unjust and presumptuous to blame the lady posthumously for not having recognised her suitor's importance as a musician and a man—or rather for having failed even to consider his possible importance in these respects. It is, after all, common knowledge that when in the bloom of youth and surrounded by admirers, women of her calling make quite different and much more substantial demands on a suitor than Beethoven was able to fulfil. They desire a husband who can live up to their own brilliance and offer them, besides his personal attractions as a lover, the social and material position which their inclinations, self-respect and thirst for happiness have always led them to covet beyond anything else. In a word, Beethoven's courtship of the young lady could not have been more hopeless. Had he been a little more world-wise, a little less naïve and above all not quite so pre-occupied with himself, he would have sensed the futility of his suit long before he decided on the step which brought him such a cruel rebuff. Seen through the eyes of a vivacious young woman who had every right to consider herself 'the button on Fortune's cap', he could hardly make any other impression than the one she so candidly and laughingly described.

The fact is—and this brings me one step nearer the truth with which I am concerned—that Beethoven did not for one moment bear the young lady any grudge for her refusal or for the frank reasons she gave him for it. This was due not to say shallowness or lack of sincerity on his part but to the fact that, notwithstanding his immense self-esteem, he was free of all vanity and blessed with an incorruptible sense of reality. He knew he was ugly; he knew there was much about him that could only seem foolish to a worldly mind; and the thought never entered his head that there might be anything unfriendly about the way in which these indisputable facts had been flung in his face. After all, *he* was seldom slow to tell others what he thought of *them*.

If it now became clear to him, in retrospect, that this wound to his self-esteem was due not to spitefulness or any other short-comings on the young lady's part but solely to the error into which his own ingenuousness and emotions had led him, this realisation did nothing to lessen his humiliation. On the contrary, it made it several degrees worse.

To be reproached—justifiably—with his own ugliness did not wound Beethoven deeply. He had long learnt not to rate the handicap of ugliness too highly. More than enough of his personality, his intellect, the power and purity of his soul showed through this ugliness to make most people blind to it. Most women, too. On many occasion his ugliness had not prevented the tenderest of homage from being paid to him, and often it had depended entirely on him how far he should enter into the kind of relationship which takes account of physical ugliness.

He reacted differently, however, to the charge of being a buffoon, to being refused not merely love but marriage on the grounds that he was too 'crack-brained' for a coveted and desirable lady to bear the idea of being joined to him in wedlock. This was where the real wound to his self-esteem lay. It was something from which there was no retreat and to which he must face up honestly and without fear of the consequences. His 'cracked-brainedness,' he knew, was merely one of the negative aspects of an artistic nature—one of the most superficial and negligible of these, even. But he had to realise that this side to him, however superficial and negligible it might be, affected many people so strongly—among them, as it happened, a cherished lady whose hand he deeply desired—that it took on the form of an insurmountable obstacle and put the propitious human partnership for which he so earnestly longed quite out of the question.

To dwell on what a high conception Beethoven had of marriage, what profound human import he ascribed to it, would be an idle undertaking. The composer of Fidelio has dealt with the subject better and more fully than anyone else could hope to do in the clumsy medium of words. When Beethoven made his proposal of marriage to that young singer, he aspired to a spiritual union with the woman he loved in which the essential part of his personality—his music and artistry—would have been sure of complete and perfect understanding: he sought the emotional atmosphere in which his artistry would be protected from all misunderstanding, from all affronts to his susceptibilities, his weaknesses and his inconsistencies.

And that is what I meant by my allusion to the 'inner truth' that this grave personal disappointment contained for Beethoven. It brought him, for the first time, face to face with the realisation that he might have to pay a terrible price for genius—the price of emotional solitude.

There is one thing to which I can honestly testify: no one could have been worse hit than he by the prospect of such a fate. In the weeks and months that followed I was deeply concerned about Beethoven, without being able to give him the least hint of how I felt for him. So hard and reserved did he show himself to all those of us who were nearest him.

[26]

SHORTLY afterwards—oblivious of the great pain she had caused him—the young singer contracted a marriage which gave her all she had hoped for. But she was not to enjoy her happiness for long. She died in her first childbed, barely three years after refusing Beethoven's hand.

I mention this because her death is bound up with an incident I can never forget.

Beethoven had called on me with a new 'cello sonata under his arm, and we had been diligently rehearsing this latest work of his preparatory to performing it before its first audience the next afternoon at the Lobkowitz' home. When we had finished and, still immersed in the music, were standing in the twilight at my study window, gazing down at the luminous candle-blossom of the chestnut trees in the courtyard, Beethoven abruptly broke the long silence.

'Have you heard? Frau G—— is dead.'

I was completely taken aback and could find no adequate reply. He had never mentioned the young woman's name in my presence, and throughout the afternoon there had been nothing in his behaviour to indicate that the sad news had already reached his ears.

'I loved her very much,' he added softly.

I turned towards him and our eyes met. With a sob he threw both arms round my neck and pressed his head violently against my breast. But just as swiftly as his feelings had overcome him, he tore himself away again—well-nigh thrusting me from him—and plunged out of the room. His hat, stick and manuscript remained lying there.

[27]

THE fact that the whole of Vienna was aware at the time of the reasons for the young singer's rejection of Beethoven and that he was consequently the butt of much coarse ridicule—especially on the part of the jealous colleagues without whom no community is ever complete—was due not to an indiscretion on the part of the young lady but rather to the care Beethoven himself took to spread the painful story. He would retail it to anyone tactless enough to broach the subject, and it obviously never occurred to him how foolishly he was acting. Astonishing though this may sound, it was not the first time he had so naïvely exposed himself to ridicule following some disappointment or abuse of his trust—just like a child that cannot understand what has happened to it.

I particularly remember a case in point shortly after his return from Berlin. During his stay there he had fallen out with Himmel, the court pianist, and was unwise enough to assume, after a reconciliation had been hastily effected, that Himmel was just as sincere about it as he was. On arriving back in Vienna he plunged into a brisk correspondence with Himmel, and the latter, a former theologian of great culture, amused himself in his replies by seeing how far he could stretch his unsuspecting colleague's credulity. His game took the form of feeding Beethoven with tall stories which he would pass on to his acquaintances as the very latest news from Berlin. One day, clearly in an attempt to end a correspondence in which he had by now lost all interest, Himmel went so far as to tender the outrageous story that somebody in Berlin had designed a lantern which made it possible for the blind to see. When Beethoven took even this legend at its face value and circulated enthusiastic accounts of the invention in Vienna, a number of us decided that things had gone far enough and urged him to decline to accept any further nonsense of that kind from Himmel.

At this Beethoven became very angry. Backward idiots like ourselves, he declared, had no idea what went on in the big world outside Vienna, and when the news of such a splendid invention did for once reach our ears we hadn't the honesty to recognise the merits of other people. Thereupon the poor fellow wrote off to tell Himmel that no one in Vienna would believe his happy tidings and that he, Himmel, must not only give him more exact details of the wonderful invention but also, if this were possible and did not involve too much expense, actually send him such a lantern so that he could convert the doubting Thomases of the imperial city on the Danube. The inevitable happened. Beethoven received an answer from Himmel which poured scorn and derision on him by the bucketful. It was a mean, perfidious document and it cut Beethoven to the quick. But now, instead of keeping Himmel's letter to himself and swallowing its contents as best he could, he hawked it round cafés and taverns, bitterly complaining of 'the dirty dog who had played such a mean trick on him'. He did not notice the malicious joy, however blatant, with which his story was generally received—just as some time later he failed to notice the way many people jeered at his unsuccessful marriage proposal. He did not grasp—and never really grasped as long as he lived—that a human being could be wicked enough to hurt others by deliberate deceit. And although it is true that the good-natured trust which he placed in his fellow beings often exceeded the bounds of common sense, it is equally true that he suffered sorely under the humiliations with which this trust was rewarded, and that these humiliations were one of the main causes of his ever-growing mistrust—a mistrust which later turned into unsociability.

[28]

THE Eroica was finished, copied and reposing on Beethoven's desk by the time it became known in Vienna that Napoleon had proclaimed himself Emperor of France. I have it from a reliable source that when Beethoven heard the news, he rushed home and tore up the title-page of his masterpiece, which was illuminated with the name of Bonaparte. As a symbolic act it was unquestionably impressive. It was admirably suited to the agitated political atmosphere of the day and contributed substantially to Beethoven's popularity. I do not doubt for one moment that he was completely in earnest when he performed it or that he sincerely desired to give striking expression to his deep disapproval of Napoleon's proclamation, since I had for years observed a process of fundamental change in Beethoven's attitude to the Corsican. The proclamation acted on Beethoven as a final revelation and confirmation of what he had long feared—that the idolised hero of humanity, the altruistic, pure, God-sent idealist he once saw in Bonaparte had become an ambitious, egoistic, power-hungry tyrant—the most odious thing he knew—an oppressor of the spiritual and moral values of free men answerable to their consciences alone. That he was now judging Napoleon just as wrongly as before, that his new hatred was just as exaggerated as his earlier enthusiasm, Beethoven did not come to realise until much later when Napoleon had rotted and died on St. Helena and the era of Metternich was teaching us how much of the Napoleonic idea of the State had been estimable and good.

Sincere though he was when making this symbolic gesture, however, I am quite certain that the word Bonaparte had long been out of place on the title-page of the Eroica, that the contents had long had nothing in common with the person of Bonaparte and that this name had, as it were, remained attached merely by force of habit and in memory of the work's first origins. When Beethoven tore up that title-page his action was less a case of ejecting Napoleon the usurper from spiritual preserves in which he had no place than of retrieving his, Beethoven's, own work from preserves into which it had inadvertently strayed. I will say just this: by the time it was complete—after five years of continuous endeavour!—the Eroica no longer had any connection with Bonaparte. On the other hand, it had every connection with the man whose importance for mankind I rate far higher than Bonaparte's—in other words, with Beethoven.

[29]

NOR is it to be wondered at that things turned out this way. Whenever a person of real individual worth sets out to glorify the ideas of another genuine personality of the same era, his undertaking is usually based from the outset on error and confusion—confusion of his own ideals with the other man's. The possibility of such a confusion is obvious, for both personalities have the same point of departure and both are born into and governed by the same problems of environment. It is my view that when Beethoven felt inspired by the young Bonaparte and reacted so quickly to Bernadotte's suggestion, he was—without being aware of it—concerned not so much with Bonaparte's ideals as with his own, which he then proceeded to project into the other's scintillating personality. Inevitably, in the course of the years, he became aware of his error and realised that Bonaparte was conforming less and less with his own ideal of humanity. This was not only because Napoleon trod the path leading up to his own proclamation as Emperor, but for the far more crucial reason that Beethoven could no longer help recognising his own ideology, its immutable self-sufficiency and the obligations that sprang from it. He experienced the moulding of his own personality with such intensity that no other theme or medium could now satisfy his urge for artistic expression.

I have often wondered what does condition the development of really great characters. For even though I have never laid claim myself to possessing a personality of any significance, the pleasure I derived from the real personalities I have encountered, and my conviction of their decisive importance to the further development of mankind, have been quite the greatest experience of my life. Today I feel that my question must remain permanently unanswered. Real personalities are a phenomenon of life arising from a divine act of creation. They originate from that sphere of things which we can only vaguely revere without being able to solve their secret with our minds. However, I do believe that I have discovered one general fact about the way true personalities emerge: each one of them, after years of groping, seeking and more or less aimless living, arrives at the point where Fate, the inexorable Anangke, confronts them with dire adversity. And at this point the decision is made whether a man who has always felt a call to special achievement can really penetrate into the realm of the extraordinary, the realm of things momentous for mankind, or whether he is to be smashed by Fate as she comes to meet him. In the lives of highly-gifted people the appearance of Anangke, of an inexorable fate, marks the moment at which their whole being either crystallises into a real personality or begins to disintegrate.

To my mind the fate which befell Beethoven is one of the hardest encountered by any man. Indeed, I can imagine nothing more terrible for a man than to be struck in the very part of his earthly equipment which he needs most in the struggle for his spiritual goal. For such an intervention by Fate is not only a handicap, an aggravation, a perpetual reminder of death for the man on whom it falls, an additional burden to bear through his life: it means the immediate and utter destruction of any possibility of further serving his own aim in life.

[30]

A DEAF musician is just as incongruous as a blind painter, a dumb orator, a legless horseman or a poet without a soul.

In order to make Beethoven's fate fully comprehensible, I shall have to descend to trivialities and say this: had Beethoven been born with the full musical genius which he in fact possessed and had yet been deaf from the very beginning of his life, he could naturally never have become a musician. To go further: had deafness struck him all at once, destroying his hearing with the same disastrous speed with which another man may be struck instantaneously blind, he would undoubtedly have been incapable from that moment onwards of carrying out his mission.

The reason why Beethoven did not surrender to the incongruous fate of being a deaf musician, but was even able to surmount it and become the real Beethoven we know today, is that his fate came upon him in a form which left him time to accept its immutability and to forge the weapons with which in due course he triumphed over the impossible.

When I speak of the 'reason', all I mean is that the long period which elapsed before his hearing was completely gone, the slowness with which this terrible process was accomplished, provided him with the essential prerequisites for his ultimate victory. The credit for this victory—and it is a moral credit of the highest order—must go entirely to Beethoven as a man.

I have never been fond of grandiloquence. I like it less today than ever I did, and hope that I am above all sentimentality and bombast if I now say that in a long life which has brought me into contact with innumerable people of varying consequence, in which I have witnessed the decline of the eighteenth century, the Napoleonic era and the rise of the present European order, I have found nothing so deserving of admiration, nothing even remotely as moving and impressive as this human drama of a deaf musician who triumphed over his fate. I will go further than that and say that to have witnessed this drama is the one thing in my life that has kept me from despairing of mankind. All the corruption and sordidness, all the frailty and mediocrity, all the complacency, cruelty, cynicism and selfishness that have passed before my eyes and left me no very high opinion of the human race—all these are outweighed and erased in my mind by the noble-mindedness, the strength and the merit of one man called Beethoven. What he achieved must be within the reach of all mankind, even though it be not for the next thousand years. Humanity cannot be hopelessly bad when one man can attain such stature and throw off such shackles.

[31]

The Eroica—to come back to the subject at last—could not emerge or become what it is before Beethoven himself had emerged from his encounter with Fate as the real Beethoven—as that completely moulded, crystallised personality who warrants my contention that the true spirit of the Eroica is quite simply 'Beethoven'—not Bonaparte, or anything else.

[32]

AND now I shall try to give the above—quite unintentionally, I did perhaps allow emotion to creep in—the tangible and factual content which will convey to my readers something of what I lived through as the friend of this great man and musician.

About the year 1800—it may have been earlier or even a little later—I became aware that all was not well with Beethoven's hearing. I noticed that even when standing right by me he would fail to react to a joke made by somebody else when I myself could not help laughing. I noticed that remarks addressed to him by other people were not being answered. I noticed that he would fail to catch certain high-pitched or softly played notes in a piece of music. And though we initially attributed these little slips to absentmindedness, it became impossible in time to close one's eyes to the truth: Beethoven was going deaf. The more this terrifying fact became apparent, the clearer it became that Beethoven was doing his utmost to conceal it—even from himself. He began drawing people's attention to particularly soft notes or distant sounds he had heard. Inevitably, he achieved precisely the opposite of what he intended, since the rest of us did not consider them by any means as faint as he tried to make out.

Even his playing showed certain changes. The first thing that struck us was how coarse his 'pianissimo'—hitherto one of his strongest points—was becoming. Then he became aware of it himself and strove to retrieve his old finesse. In doing so, however, he was entirely dependent on the sensitiveness of his fingertips, for his own ear no longer heard fine tones, particularly in a high key, and when he was handling a strange instrument it was even possible for the notes he thought he was producing not to be heard at all.

After a time one sensed that he had given up trying to delude himself but was all the more intent on concealing his loss of hearing from other people. In our loyalty we all entered into the spirit of this tragic game. We had quickly grasped that the best way of helping him was not to speak louder but only more distinctly. Similarly, when music was played, one had to avoid excessive volume, as very loud notes were beginning to hurt him.

I need not stress that we, his friends, followed all this with deep anxiety and anguish. All the more so, indeed, as certain ill-disposed persons had by now become aware of the grave state of affairs and were already giving vent to their satisfaction by all sorts of spiteful remarks. Wherever there was a bold or even unusual turn of harmony in any of his compositions, these people now pounced on the chance to observe, often only too audibly, that no one could wonder at such aberrations in a musician whose ears were failing him. At the same time none of us dared to broach the matter to Beethoven himself. Indeed, I am convinced to this day that if anyone had had the courage to do so he would have paid for it with the loss of Beethoven's friendship.

Then, one evening early in 1802, I received an unexpected call from Beethoven. I say 'unexpected' because he normally went to bed early; when he did occasionally stay up late, it was usually in convivial company and over a bottle of wine. It was only too clear from his demeanour that there was something on his mind for which he could not find the right words. He talked for a while in an awkward and desultory fashion; he tinkled a little on my piano; he told, without any attempt at introduction, a few broad anecdotes that were quite out of keeping with his mood; he grumbled about one or two real or imaginary enemies; and finally he turned to leave without my having the least indication of what he had come for. I was already prepared for him to go with his mission unaccomplished, so to speak—as if he had come for no other purpose than, in his own words, to 'pass the time of day'—when, his hand already on the doorknob, he turned round again. Then, with a look I shall never forget, he asked in an apparently casual tone:

'I suppose it's already very obvious?'

I knew immediately what he meant, but did not dare admit it.

'How do you mean?' I countered. 'What is supposed to be obvious?'

'Don't try to humbug me,' he said quietly, coming back into the room again and standing there with his hands behind his back. 'I release you from any further efforts in that direction—when we are alone, that is. What I want to know is whether it's already very noticeable?'

I had control of myself by now. And since I had learnt to fall in with his moods unquestioningly, I replied in the same tone of apparent composure and indifference which he had adopted.

'Not excessively so . . .' I said, 'but all the same. . . . It varies, too. It's more pronounced some days than others.'

'Yes, I know!' he exclaimed impulsively, but still very softly. 'There are days when I almost dare to hope . . .'

Suddenly the words burst out of me, without my being able to stem them.

'*Lieber, verehrter, bester Freund,*' I cried, 'you surely can't mean that you . . . It *must* be only a temporary ailment! Surely it can be cured? Haven't you consulted any doctors? —I beg you—do put my mind at rest!'

For a long time Beethoven was silent. With one eyebrow raised, he gazed at me in a way that was half pitying, half dispassionate. Bravo, very creditable, that look seemed to say—but what do *you* know of the hell I bear in my heart . . . ? When he spoke again, his voice was hard, almost forbidding.

'I've already talked to the doctors about it. There's no question of a cure. The only question is whether it can be checked. . . . The next few months will decide that.'

All at once something blazed up in his eyes that was like hatred and naked fear combined. Deeply moved, I stepped towards him with hands outstretched.

But Beethoven turned mutely away and left me without a word of farewell.

[33]

DURING those years I was usually away from Vienna for the summer months, partly on duty in Budapest with my chief, Count Pallfy, partly on leave with friends or relatives on their Hungarian estates. In that summer of 1802, so critical for Beethoven, I had not succeeded, as in previous years, in persuading him to accept the invitations to Hungary that I had arranged for him. Consequently I was out of touch with him until my return to Vienna. I learnt that he had chosen the wine-growing village of Heiligenstadt near Vienna as his place of residence and was devoting himself to his work there in more or less complete seclusion. I was happy at this news, for it allowed me to hope that the verdict on his ear ailment was a favourable one and that Beethoven had found his peace of mind once more.

I returned to Vienna at the beginning of October, not suspecting what alarms and unpleasantness were in store for me.

Before I go into further detail, I should mention that one year previously, towards the end of 1801, a certain Ferdinand Ries had arrived in Vienna and been accepted by Beethoven as a pupil. This Ferdinand Ries was a youth on the threshold of manhood—seventeen or eighteen years old, perhaps, and the son of a Bonn musician who had once given Beethoven violin lessons. Judging by the warmth and friendship with which Beethoven took the young man under his wing, he must have had the most grateful memories of old Ries. In any case, young Ries was an uncommonly likeable lad with a bright and cheerful disposition, and he reciprocated Beethoven's paternal kindness with quite fervent devotion, besides being a source of great pleasure to him by reason of his abundant talent. Ferdinand Ries is the first in that series of *famuli* and *familiares* whose diligence became more and more indispensable to Beethoven and who, as the years went by, were of very real assistance to him in relieving him of the need to worry about everyday trivialities.

I was unpacking my valise and trunks, preparatory to settling into my apartment for the winter, when this same Ferdinand Ries burst into my bedroom in front of the servant who was about to announce him.

'*Ach*, thank God you are back!' he cried, throwing himself into my arms and breaking into the kind of unrestrained sobbing which means that an unbearable emotional tension has reached breaking point.

I was thoroughly alarmed by all this. For I knew Ries well enough to guess that he would not thus distress himself without some grave reason. And that his agitation and fright could concern none but Beethoven I had realised before even the first cry escaped him.

I let the young man weep to his heart's content, as there was no point in bombarding him with questions until he calmed down a little. Taking him into my study, I made him sit down and spoke a few soothing words to him.

'You must pull yourself together, my young friend,' I told him. 'I realise something has badly frightened you and that you have come to seek my help. I know, too, for whom you need my help, and you did right to come to me. But now you must take told of yourself and tell me what you are afraid of—otherwise we may lose valuable time. . . .'

Under my coaxing the youth soon regained his composure. By asking him a few questions—and possibly also by my calm manner—I soon persuaded him to give me a reasonably coherent account of the trouble.

He had spent the whole summer with Beethoven in Heiligenstadt. To all appearance, Beethoven had been thoroughly enjoying life, despite the great pressure under which he worked.

'He's written a new symphony,' the lad explained, 'and a number of piano sonatas, too. Wonderful things they are—I copied them all out for him and know them by heart. . . .'

'Yes, yes,' I urged, 'but what . . . ?'

It now appeared that there had, after all, been occasional brief spells of dejection and moroseness.

'What about?' I asked.

A deep flush spread over the young man's pale cheeks and, as if he had something shameful to tell, he began a hesitant and almost stuttering explanation.

'For example,' he said, '. . . one day we were out for a walk together. It was a wonderful morning . . . and when a shepherd who was looking after his sheep on a hill nearby blew a few trills on his pipe, I quite naturally said how much I liked the sound—how well it suited the freshness of the morning.

'The maestro stared at me and said "What shepherd?"

' "Over there," I said, "by the edge of the wood," and pointed the spot out to him.

' "He blew?" he asked me then. "And you heard him?"

'Then it slipped out. "Of course!" I said. "He blew quite loudly!"

'Hardly were the words out of my mouth when I saw what damage I had done—fool that I was! The maestro turned on his heel and went back to the village. I followed him, pleading with him as I went. He didn't speak another word to me, and I might as well have sunk into the earth for all the notice he took of me. . . . It was not until the next day that he paid any attention to me and gave me some work to copy.'

'I see. Has this sort of thing often happened?'

'Not through any fault of mine after that! I would rather have bitten off my tongue. . . .'

'All right,' I said, 'go on with the story!'

'Two or three times since he has sat brooding in the same sullen way—for three days on end, on one occasion. That time he refused to let me go out with him on his walks. . . .'

'And since then?' I prompted.

'Yesterday . . .' Ries began hesitantly.

Then he swallowed hard and went pluckily on. 'Yesterday it started again—but worse than usual. As early as daybreak I heard him pacing up and down his room and muttering to himself, and before I could get up to see what was wrong I heard the door of his room slam as he went downstairs. I looked out of the window and saw him hurrying away without a hat or coat. When I called after him he didn't—or wouldn't—hear me. Later I found a note in his room: "Gone to Vienna to see the doctor." He came back late that evening with the mail coach, looking as I've never seen him look before—pale and shattered and with a strange glow in his eyes. Though I thought at first that he hadn't seen me, he let me walk beside him. I didn't dare say a word the whole way home. He went up to his room and lay down on his bed without a word—still fully clothed and with dirty boots. I sat down by him and tried to take his hand, but he snatched it away and lay motionless, staring at the ceiling. He stayed like that for hours. Once he whispered something that I didn't rightly catch, though I thought I heard the word "Finished". At last I could endure it no longer. Kneeling by his bed, I cried: "Maestro . . . maestro! Do speak just one word to me!"—At that he laid his hand on my head and said: "Poor lad . . . off you go to bed now . . . this is no concern of yours." —And when I didn't immediately rise, he said it again: "Go away! I've no use for you now, you or anyone else!" —That left me no choice but to get up and leave. . . .'

Again there were big tears running down the poor boy's cheeks.

'Calm yourself,' I urged him. 'You must tell me more. You haven't finished yet.'

Cold fear was already clutching at my throat.

'I couldn't sleep, I couldn't go to bed. I took off my shoes and spent the whole night walking up and down outside his room in stockinged feet, listening for the least sound of movement. It must have been about four o'clock when I heard him get up. He lit a lamp, and I heard him shift a chair. . . . Then I peeped through the keyhole. . . .'

'Well?'

'He was sitting at his table, writing. . . .'

'Go on.'

'I waited for a long time, and in the end could stand it no longer. I softly lifted the latch and stepped over the threshold. He looked up—saw me standing there—and said not a word. He just stared fixedly in my direction—with a look—a look I cannot describe—so distant, so far, far away—so terribly cold and strange. . . . A terrible fear seized me then. . . . Closing the door, I dashed to my room, put my boots on again and ran all the way here—to you.'

Clenching both hands round the armrests of his chair, the young man half rose and stared into my face with eyes wide with fear.

'He'll lay hands on himself,' he shouted. 'You must help, or he'll lay hands on himself!'

Strange as it may sound, the very moment the young man screamed out his fear—the same fear that had been wringing my own heart—I felt freed. Suddenly I was sure that what we both feared had not and would not come to pass. And the relief which surged over me was passed on to him. I spoke words of consolation, I said how grateful I was to him for coming to see me, that I quite understood why he should seek my help, but that I was certain that his fears would prove groundless.

'You are very young,' I said. 'You have reason, every reason, to be utterly terrified. But I believe—in fact I'm convinced—that you're mistaken. I've known Beethoven much longer than you have. I'm no less fond of him than you are—but my knowledge of him is different from yours. Beethoven is the last man to do anything desperate. None the less, you're right to think that we shouldn't leave him alone. We'll drive straight out to Heiligenstadt to see him. When we get there we'll act quite naturally, as if you hadn't fetched me. You'll see—it won't be necessary to explain my presence. In that way we'll make quite certain that I am right—that nothing has happened or is going to happen.'

I rang for my servant and told him to have a coach and pair outside the door in an hour to take us out to Heiligenstadt.

'And now you must relax—completely,' I told young Ries.

Gradually his features regained their normal placidity, and as soon as we were in the coach he fell into the deep, peaceful sleep of exhaustion.

[34]

When we reached Heiligenstadt Beethoven was no longer at home. At the house where he lodged we learnt that he had slept well into the morning and then gone out.

I proposed to young Ries that he should remain in Beethoven's lodgings—which were, after all, his own as well—while I went to the inn to arrange my accommodation. And this we proceeded to do.

Afterwards I decided to take a walk. It was not yet too late in the day; the sun was mild, and I was glad of my own company for a while. So I strolled through the vineyards, which gave every promise of a rich yield that year. The vines were heavy with grapes, and it could not be long before the merry bustle of the harvest began.

On a tiny hill hardly twenty feet high stood a little chapel by an enormous lime tree; under the tree was a bench; and it was on this bench that I found Beethoven when I reached the top of the hill.

His head was bare. Though tired-looking, he had not the aspect of a man about to take leave of this life.

'Why, it's the musical count!' he exclaimed, slapping the seat to the left of him as a sign that I should sit down. 'I've been wondering all day long who'd be the first to appear. That silly boy Ries has run away. . . .'

'I've brought him back with me,' I told him. 'He was very frightened. He's in your lodgings, waiting for you.'

'He can go on waiting. And tomorrow I shall give him a piece of my mind. What did he imagine there was to be frightened about? The fact that I sat up at night writing? Must I ask his permission next time?'

'He happens to have had a bad fright,' I retorted. 'And certainly not through any lack of affection for you. Judge grown men by their actions, if you wish: when dealing with anyone who's still half a child you'd do better to go by his heart. . . .'

Beethoven looked up at me wide-eyed, but said nothing for a while.

'How right you are!' he said at last. 'I suppose a man isn't fully mature till he no longer allows his heart to scare him out of his wits. A bad thing, the human heart . . .'

'A good heart,' I interrupted, 'is liable to cause a great deal of trouble.'

'Come!' said Beethoven. 'Let us stroll for a while through this beautiful evening!'

He rose to his feet and turned to go. I followed him in silence.

When we were on a level path again he slipped a hand through my arm—an intimate gesture which it was rare for him to make. I could plainly feel him leaning on me and sensed how glad he was to be guided.

Even his voice had an unusual softness as he began to speak again.

'I was writing my will last night when that silly young oaf ran off to fetch you. I didn't write it because I was contemplating dying. I wrote it because I had come very close to Death—and because the terror of it was still in my soul. It isn't every day that one can think of the End and all that it means. . . .'

Clearly he did not expect a reply. When he spoke again, he sounded more like a man talking to himself than one seeking to unbosom himself to another. Or perhaps he unbosomed himself only because he felt it safe to do so in my presence.

'I am doomed, Zmeskall,' he said. 'There's no longer any hope. In a few years I shall be so deaf that they'll be able to let off a cannon behind me without my even batting an eyelid. . . . At first I thought all the doctors were idiots—until it occurred to me that if they really were it must be God's will that they should be. And since a musician can't live without ears, I thought I was finished. Finished because God willed it.'

Again he was silent for a while as he paced slowly along on my arm.

Then, all of a sudden, he halted.

'And it was that,' he said, 'which set me thinking. God's will can't be the End. God couldn't have sent me into the world, equipped as I am to make music, merely to dash my legs from under me on the last lap and to leave me lying by the wayside like some useless carrion. And if God couldn't have willed this, I reasoned, he must have given me something else besides my genius—something that would enable me to survive. It was then that I delved into my innermost soul to find what *had* to be in me somewhere—to find what I needed even more than my genius if I were to go on living and to fulfil God's will. . . .

'It was terribly hard, Zmeskall. I shied and bucked like a restive horse. I wanted to break loose with all the strength of my wretched heart—but in the end I had to face up to it. I've given in—and now the yoke's on my shoulders. . . .'

Quite softly, only just audibly, the words came through his lips: 'It means renunciation . . . renunciation of everything that makes life happy: people, friendship, love—all the simple, modest joys of life. I must renounce all the things that can ever captivate a man—success, fame, distinction, honours—everything that hearts good and bad desire so ardently. . . .'

I was shaken to the very depths of my soul.

'Beethoven!' I cried, 'Beethoven, my dear, good friend—you go too far! You see too much of the dark side of things. You're letting depression get the better of you. You'll learn to take a different view of it all before long!'

I said it in spite of myself—against my better judgment—only because I could not bear to leave it unsaid.

Beethoven waited until my outburst was over and then looked deep into my eyes. For all his gravity there was something very near mockery in his gaze.

'*So?*' His voice, hitherto so gentle, had a dry inflection now. 'I'm letting depression get the better of me, am I? I look too much on the dark side, do I? I hardly think so.'

'I'm not deaf yet!' he went on vehemently. 'I still have a few years to go before these accursed ears forsake me completely! And these few years—God's left them to me so that I may achieve what His will demands! I'm going to use them to the full! I'm not going to expend one breath, one heartbeat, one thought or sensation on anything else but my mission, my life work! Don't you understand? What can you know of me if you can't grasp that?'

'You've already produced much that is great and

magnificent!' I retorted just as warmly. 'You're taking your own achievements in vain!'

'Fiddlesticks! Great and magnificent indeed! Anyone else with my talents could have done the same . . .'

'But no one else *has* your talents!' I interrupted.

He ignored the objection.

'It's now—now—that matters!' he cried with growing agitation. 'It's now that we shall see whether I've understood God! Whether I've rightly grasped why He let me go deaf! Why He brought this dreadful affliction upon me. . . .

'*Despite everything* are the words constantly in my mind. With this phrase I'll uproot trees and move whole mountains. . . . With this phrase I'll give music a completely new aspect. . . . I'll show all of you that genius is a trifle, a mere plaything—I'll show you what talent can turn into in the hands of a man who spits into the face of Fate!'

He had worked himself into an ecstasy of fury. He stretched his clenched fist up to heaven and thundered out his distress into the world around him.

'Let Fate shackle me to the cliffs! Let it think it has broken me! God is stronger than Fate! God gave me strength to find Him even though I was in shackles! The few years remaining to me will show who I am! And if my heart goes to pieces in the process—let the Devil himself pick up the fragments! I shan't stoop to help him. . . . My *work* is all I want—and I shall succeed!'

He was trembling in every limb, and suddenly I saw all the colour drain from his face. He was near collapse. I laid a firm arm round his shoulders and pressed him to me, gradually feeling his agitation die away. For one brief moment, overcome by an intense exhaustion, he laid his head on my breast. Then, slowly disengaging himself from my arm, he straightened up again.

'Let us move on,' he said—only to change his mind after a few steps and come to a halt again.

'You've been an upright friend to me all these years, Zmeskall. I thank you for it. From now on I can have no friends. From now on I can only know people of use to my work—for I can let nothing else in this world distract me. . . .'

Deeply moved, he pressed my hand. Then the shadow of a smile flitted across his face.

'When I'm deaf, though—quite deaf—when everything lies behind me and I'm quite useless to the world—you might look after me again then. . . .'

[35]

No, he did not want to go out again that day, Beethoven told me as we approached his lodgings. Ries could fetch him a light meal from the inn, after which he would retire early. With that I was dismissed.

It was by now a little late to drive back to Vienna; the horses would be tired, for one thing. And—one never knew—it was perhaps just as well to remain in Heiligenstadt for this one night.

The dining-room of the inn was still empty when I entered. I ordered something to eat and had not been at table long before young Ries came in with a gay flush in his cheeks.

'Oh, Herr von Zmeskall,' he cried, 'I do thank you! What a good thing it was you came! He's quite himself again—*Gott sei Dank!*'

Blushing furiously, but with shining eyes, he went on to explain, in answer to my inquiring look:

'He gave me such a scolding—in the strongest possible language. . . .' And, stuttering with laughter, he added: 'He even boxed my ears!'

'I see,' I said, laughing myself now. 'Then everything

seems to be in order again.' And I shook the good fellow warmly by the hand.

'I must hurry now,' said Ries. 'He doesn't like to be kept waiting when he's hungry.'

'Off you go then . . . there's sure to be something ready in the kitchen—I say Ries,' I said, calling him back, 'I think it would be better to say nothing to anyone about what you witnessed yesterday and today.'

'But of course not!' he cried. 'Never—never—as long as I live!'

Thereupon he disappeared into the rooms at the back.

Later on the premises began to fill up as peasants and artisans returning from their day's work foregathered for their evening drink. They were good, sturdy figures, these self-assured, prosperous-looking men, and it did me good to listen to their cheerful raillery.

Next morning I asked for the carriage at six, and only a few hours later I was sitting in my office, back in the harness of everyday routine once more.

[36]

Were the expression not so trivial, this would be the appropriate place to recall that no soup is ever eaten as hot as it is cooked. Indeed, the contrast between the inner reality of a profound emotional shock, together with the decisions born of it, and the rather more indulgent and casual manner in which these decisions tend to be carried out in the practical conditions of daily life is perhaps never more striking than in the case of a remarkable personality, whose *pendulum animae* is capable of the widest swings.

It is perfectly true that those who were unaware of the

depth and rigour of the crisis through which Beethoven had passed, and were content to regard him as an eccentric musical genius, could detect hardly any change in his outward way of life after that October in 1802. He had, after all, always been fanatically industrious, and the fact that he was now in the habit of following up days and weeks of grim, implacable solitude with hours of either boisterous and ribald merry-making or serious, passionate discussion with clever, able-minded men—this fact did not, to an outsider, convey the picture of any great inner transformation.

The truth remains, nevertheless, that the immense categorical imperative which Beethoven had imposed on himself, and the breath-taking race between his frenzied labours and failing hearing, henceforth dominated his every deed and aspiration, the times he woke and slept, and even the few hours of recreation and relaxation which he allowed himself. So complete and exclusive was this domination that even today, long after all this happened, I am still lost in admiration for the way Beethoven's constitution endured such reckless overtaxing of his physical and mental resources for years on end.

In one respect, thank God, the doctors advising Beethoven had proved wrong: his inexorable progress towards total deafness took place much more slowly than they expected. In fact sixteen whole years elapsed before that moment was reached when—as Beethoven himself had so drastically put it—'they could let off a cannon behind him without his batting an eyelid.' And I might as well say here that before those sixteen years were up, a new crisis occurred in Beethoven's artistic development and confronted him with quite a different set of problems and decisions, as a result of which total deafness had by no means the same outcome as he had foreseen in the year 1802. Of this I shall say more at the proper time. Initially—indeed, for ten whole years up to 1812—his life was entirely dominated by his inner tension and a fanatical resolve to extract from himself, at the greatest possible speed and by ruthless exploitation of his vital energies, the very last, the very utmost of what he had to give—by a resolve to create, in the time left to him, a work of such significance and magnitude that, when the end finally came, he would be able to save himself from despair in the consolation of that work, in the lasting fruit of a life fulfilled.

It is astonishing how most people—among them many sensitive, intelligent men and women with plenty of experience of life—will let the most remarkable phenomena occur under their very noses without realising what a unique drama they have witnessed, without even wondering how such a thing could have come about. I will put it this way: in the ten years from 1802 to 1812 Beethoven produced one masterpiece after another in such rapid succession and dizzy profusion that his promise to give music a completely new aspect came strikingly true. And yet, to my knowledge, no one was particularly surprised by this incredible achievement. Everyone was content to remark that Beethoven had 'quite unusual talent, you know.' And, setting their minds at rest with this phrase—which, strictly speaking, meant absolutely nothing—people found it 'perfectly natural' that a man with such 'talent' should accomplish things for which Beethoven had had to struggle so hard.

Let us take a closer look.

In those ten years there came into being, from the Eroica to the Eighth, six whole symphonies, each of them a paragon of beauty and depth. Then there was the Fidelio. There were two piano concertos, a violin concerto, a triple concerto. There were piano sonatas, violin sonatas, trios, quartets and numerous overtures—all of them works of great moment. And, concurrently, Beethoven produced a wealth of lesser compositions—written by way of relaxation, as it were. Not one of these is without merit, and many are delightfully original.

In listing these works I have expressly refrained from going into details about their intrinsic relationship or outward diversity. I mention them simply to indicate their scope and volume. No one capable of a reasonably accurate estimate of what they comprise will deny that to cram so much into the brief span of ten years—of 120 months, of 500 weeks—is nothing short of a miracle. I invite anyone to study a list of Beethoven's output during that period and to calculate on that basis how many months, weeks and days each individual work must have taken him. Even if all these compositions were just melodious rubbish, it would still be an unusual accomplishment. The fact, however, that they embrace twenty, even thirty works, each of which, in its own way, gives music 'a completely new aspect'—that, as I shall never tire of repeating, makes those ten years in Beethoven's life pre-eminent in the history of intellectual endeavour.

[37]

It was the Eroica which introduced this series of works. It came into existence in the spring and summer of 1803, in the same deathless form as it has today. It is the first complete, mature fruit of that inner development which culminated in the crystallisation of Beethoven's personality in the crisis of Autumn 1802.

Right up to the end of his life—in spite of the Missa and the Ninth Symphony—Beethoven himself regarded the Eroica as his best work. Incorrect though this assessment undoubtedly is—incorrect in the purely logical sense, for the Eroica and the Ninth cannot, as masterpieces, be compared—it is very understandable. The Eroica was where Beethoven discovered himself; it was the first in that long series of works which he wrested from Fate and in which, in defiance of Fate, he found God. It was the first work in whose creation he could allow himself to feel immortal. For no one but he could have written it: no musician will ever succeed in doing more than he did here for the first time—in setting the imprint of his soul on all humanity.

[38]

AND now I have said what the Eroica really is.

It is not only a work of art of consummate beauty, created by the infallible hand of a master.

It is also a message, a gospel. It is a testimony of the spirit which is alone able to give life the thing which makes it bearable: a purpose transcending the confines of life and death.

[39]

WHEN hoary old men prefer the days of their youth and early manhood to those of their old age and have anything to say in praise of them, they lay themselves open to pitying smiles or even outright scorn from the younger generation. This is a risk I am prepared to take. If the youth of today derides me, I shall merely conclude that my views are right.

I am certain that those of us who were in the prime of life in the ten years when Beethoven was proclaiming his message opened our very hearts and souls to it. I am certain that we heard it and that it moved, thrilled and moulded us. Though everyone may not have been affected in the same way, we all sensed its purpose. We felt the eternal truth it breathed.

Who, then, were 'we'? I could mention twenty, thirty, forty names. They are the names of distinguished men from all walks of life who were so captivated by Beethoven and his message as to feel linked together in a kind of secret understanding which transcended whatever else might divide them—united in their appreciation of the rare gift conferred on themselves and mankind every time Beethoven brought out a new work. But in addition—and this is probably of far greater significance—there were the many hundreds and thousands of people who, whenever a new Beethoven work was played, invariably accorded it the reception it rightly deserved. This anonymous public of Viennese music-lovers needed no other aid to the assimilation of Beethoven's message than its own instinct and readiness to comprehend. I consider it proof of the high cultural standard of Vienna—the Vienna of those ten or twelve years before the Congress—that despite the unusual demands which Beethoven's works made on the listener's receptivity, he found in our city that echo of sympathy for their boldness, for their ethical and emotional content, which spurred him on to ever greater and more ambitious efforts.

I have no fear of being contradicted when I declare that today—indeed, for many years past—all that remains of this appreciation, enthusiasm and sympathy is what we few old survivors have been able to carry over into this era of shallowness and abdication.

To be sure, the public of today still has a certain respect, a certain awe for the name of Beethoven, and most people would take care not to show themselves up by any deprecation of his work—but the truth is that the broad mass of Viennese, like most of the gentlemen who set the public trend of music, find Beethoven's work far too serious and exacting, and also thoroughly dull. Above all, they no longer hear the message, the gospel it proclaims. They have become apathetic. Their souls are lethargic, complacent and superficial. Performances of Beethoven symphonies—we hear them seldom enough nowadays—resemble sermons in the desert which fade away—*cum grano salis*—unheard.

Merely the grumblings of an old man, you think? Then I will try to prove both contentions—that about the greater receptiveness of the Viennese of 1810 and the other about the depressing lack of discernment shown by the Viennese of 1830.

Let us take the latter first.

What kind of music is played in modern Vienna? Rossini, and still more Rossini. Whom does one go to hear play? Hummel, Moscheles and other elegant masters of the keyboard. And the shallower the rondos, concertos, fantasias and variations that are offered, the more tumultuous the applause. I am not a spiteful man and will mention no names. But when I asked one of the most famous pianists why he did not play any Beethoven—the sonatas in F, C sharp and D minor, for example—he replied: 'It would be love's labour lost, my dear sir! *I* would put my fingers out of joint while the public merely yawned. . . .'

But two years ago, here in Vienna, there died in poverty and solitude, his merits unrecognised, a man who barely managed to have a small part of his work published without starving. Whole stacks of his masterpieces—unprinted and never yet performed—are fast collecting dust at the home of his surviving brother. That man was Franz Schubert.

Is this proof enough? I think so.

And twenty years ago?

In those days Beethoven's work did not bore people. One did not put one's fingers out of joint playing his sonatas. His symphonies and chamber music were acclaimed with deep and genuine feeling.

But I have more impressive evidence than that of the spirit of the day—evidence conclusive enough to impress even the most shallow of philistines.

The scheme had already been noised abroad even before

a summons to Beethoven to visit Jerôme's court at Cassel brought it to fruition: three eminent gentlemen banded together and pledged themselves in a legal contract to pay Beethoven an annuity of 6,000 florins till the end of his days, on the one condition that he stayed in Vienna. They did so without laying any claim to the material returns from his work, without expressing the least wish—let alone giving any directions—on his future output. And this commitment was undertaken at a time when all of us, including those three gentlemen, had no shadow of doubt that in all probability Beethoven would be stone deaf in the next few years and thereafter incapable of any further creative activity. In other words, he was likely to go on living for decades after the source of his art had dried up. People may object here that Beethoven's benefactors were wealthy gentlemen who could well afford 6,000 florins between them. Such objections are easy enough to make in retrospect. I, for one, have noticed that rich people are as a rule far more disinclined to part with their money than the less well-to-do. Most of all, I know that in pecuniary matters, in particular, the *deed* is the ultimate pointer to a man's mental outlook: people of means can advance no stronger proof of the genuineness of their convictions than by giving money away in support of them.

Another thing I do not want to forget here—perhaps it weighs even more than the financial sacrifice of those three great gentlemen—is the way musicians who were generally as poor as church mice regularly and gratuitously put themselves at Beethoven's disposal for performances of his works. They counted themselves happy to be of service to the man they revered as the uncrowned king of music.

[40]

I DO not believe that the present generation will ultimately prove right in its indifference to Beethoven's work and human message.

On the contrary, I am convinced that the ideals which Beethoven set forth will come into their own once more. I am convinced that the *noblesse oblige* inherent in the concept of human existence will arise again once the wounds torn in our continent by the last century are healed and a generation has grown up with redder blood in its veins and hearts that beat more manfully. And because I am convinced that Beethoven was one of the greatest protagonists of these ideals—if not the greatest of all—to have lived in my age, I am striving today, as far as my diminished strength allows, to preserve an authentic picture of his personality—to preserve it through the present era of impotence and shallowness into a future animated, through a reawakened understanding of his work, by the desire to rediscover the *man* who wrote such magnificent, virile and unique music.

[41]

OF the eighteenth century—whatever faults it may have had—one must say this: it was one of those rare eras which contrived to reinstate man and his intrinsic dignity at the centre of all perception and as the criterion of all values. It was one of the eras to discover that for man the concept of freedom is synonymous with moral restraint and that if only man will give this perception its full due, he needs no abstract, fictitious, artificially established or revelational agency to guide him to Eternity and the spiritual liberation that supersedes all temporal suffering and doubts—he needs none of the things tabooed by ecclesiastical dogma, by political, obscurantist, spiritualist or other sects and organisations. The man of the eighteenth century, in his best and truly representative form, believed in himself and his human worth. He needed no other belief in order to feel linked with God and Eternity, for he bore God and Eternity within himself. God and Eternity were for him simply the expression of what was best and purest within him—they were the expression of the spiritual principle which had generated his humanity and dignity.

The man of the eighteenth century, in his best and truly representative form, possessed what the present age lacks in such depressing measure—nobleness of mind. He knew respect, but not fear. He knew pride, but not vanity. He knew freedom, but not licence, he knew power, but not despotism; he knew the terrible adversities of Fate, but he also knew his own capacity for making light of them. He knew all this at the very last as an ideal, and he believed this ideal to be attainable, both for the individual and for mankind as a whole.

All this—the whole ideal of the human being convinced of his own worth, dignity and moral strength, of his capacity for happiness and his link with eternity—is contained in Beethoven's music. One can go further and say that the sole reason why his music ever came into existence was to proclaim, propagate and realise this ideal and, by the very fact of having attained it, to prove to mankind that it was no phantom but a reality—perhaps the only reality there is: the reality of the Spirit, the Eternal and the Absolute.

[42]

At its outset the French Revolution was essentially nothing other than an attempt to translate these ideals, so finely poised on the summit of human thought, into the broad reality of everyday life—a heroic undertaking inspired by a pious faith. Its gravest error was to suppose that the popular masses were ripe for this ideal and would prove equal to its demands from natural instinct once they were freed from the yoke of obscurantism. And it was here that the Revolution slipped from the control of its authentic leaders into the hands of the mob. Thus did the Revolution lead to chaos.

Then came the man who knew that the eighteenth-century ideals of the French Revolution, the ideals of those who had originally set out to lead it, could be saved for mankind only if this chaos were first checked and law and order restored. There is no means in this world of attaining such an end save by military might and soldierly discipline, save by unconditional observance of the hierarchic principle of unquestioning obedience. This saviour from chaos could only be a man of supreme military genius.

I personally have not the slightest doubt that initially Napoleon was absolutely serious about regarding the politico-military rehabilitation of France as merely a method of salving the original ideals of the Revolution and the eighteenth century. That is why, at the beginning of his career, the hearts of all men anxious to see these humane ideals preserved, whether Frenchmen or not, went out to him in sympathy. Then, however, that factor emerged of which examples abound in the history of mankind: power and force are so closely related, namely, that the man on whom great power has descended is turned—mostly against his will—from power to violence. But violence provokes violence. And the upshot of that is only too familiar to us all now that we have drained the cup to the last bitter dregs: devastation, exhaustion, weakness and misery. And then, in succession to the material chaos of which the might that became despotism was born, comes spiritual chaos, the loss of those very ideals with which the whole vicious circle began.

I use the words 'spiritual chaos' quite deliberately, for it is hardly an exaggeration to apply them to the spectacle with which any impartial observer is confronted today.

In France we have had the farce whereby a Louis XVIII was able to regain the throne of his fathers only after signing and swearing to a constitution which bears all the hallmarks of revolutionary phraseology—a constitution which is a slap in the face to everything he and his traditions represent. No wonder this farce burst like a soap-bubble a few months ago.

The rest of Europe, however, the Europe of the Holy Alliance, is dominated by the very thing Napoleon's conquerors claimed to be fighting more than anything else—brute force. Present-day Europe is under the sway of that insidious, scheming tyranny which will go to any lengths to suppress and discredit the spiritual freedom that is so aware of its own dignity. This obscurantist tyranny is apparently best suited to lead a spent and despondent humanity.

I bear a man like Metternich no grudge for being merely a combination of the Duke of Otranto and Count Talleyrand—without the authentic cynicism of the former or the accomplished intellect of the latter. Nor do I blame the people of today, after all they have undergone, for the fact that a man like Metternich should have succeeded in setting himself up as the controller of their destinies. But I refuse to regard the present situation of the German people as anything but a pitiable and—I most sincerely hope—temporary depression—an ailment brought on by exhaustion, an ebbing of the vital spirits.

[43]

BEETHOVEN was certainly not a very cultured man, and his intellectual pre-occupation with the complex problems surrounding him was limited in the extreme. I can safely say that he cared hardly a tinker's damn for such things. Only when they appealed to his instincts, his emotions, his heart or his moral convictions did he take any interest in the turbulent events of his day. Many a time he would fervently take sides in some matter and then, ingenuously following a change in his feelings, condemn a thing with the same vehemence as he had extolled it the day before. It was precisely in his instincts, his emotions and his convictions that he never for one moment allowed himself to be distracted. He is, in my experience, the only person to have safely borne the lofty ideals of Man, his dignity and his intrinsic worth, through the terrible disintegration of the last four decades. He bore them through unharmed and unchanged, imperturbably clinging to what was for him a pure and simple truth. Throughout the disorders, vacillations, surrenders and betrayed beliefs of this period he has preserved for mankind what is timeless and immortal in eighteenth-century ideals. He did so by giving these values an expression which is just as timeless and immortal in its artistic beauty as the ideals themselves.

And that—namely to clothe the truth that was his own truth in a garment of deathless beauty—is exactly what Beethoven conceived to be the purpose of his life.

The fact that I regard the human ideals to which Beethoven subscribed as especially sublime and precious and am personally disinclined to budge one inch from this belief—well, that is my own personal concern, and I admit that others, in theory, may dispute the worth of these ideals. But that a man could stand up for them as Beethoven did, that he could be so imbued with them as to sacrifice everything and shoulder the most grievous misfortune for their sake, that nothing, not even the most bewildering and cataclysmic of world events, could prevent him from accomplishing a titanic feat of labour and from clothing these ideals in the garment of a supremely beautiful testimony which is valid for all time—that he was able to do this gives me the unquestionable right to use a term which translates him into the Parnassus of mankind and the lap of divinity: he was *great*.

[44]

I WOULD permit myself to add one further point here: the term 'greatness' also implies completeness and variety. No one can lay claim to greatness, least of all an artist, if he lacks some essential component in the scale of human qualities and human experience.

Nothing is further from my intentions than to select a number of Beethoven's works and to launch into a professorial disquisition on their extra- and supra-musical implications. I am a confirmed opponent of such practices—and I hasten to add that Beethoven himself sharply refused to countenance any attempts to interpret his compositions in terms of programme-music. 'You're not supposed to *think* about it,' he would say, 'you're supposed to *feel* it. If you can't do that it either means that I'm a useless bungler *or* that you are unmusical philistines. . . .'

His language was music. And the essence of music is that it approaches the soul direct, needing neither the detours of abstract thought nor the logic and descriptive power of words.

But at the same time one must be allowed to say this

much: Beethoven's work left no aspect of human nature untouched. From supreme pathos to the simplest of feelings, from the most humble to the most sublime, from the most intimate communion with nature to the ultimate twilight of the soul, from solemn veneration to the most unrestrained merriment, from true devotion to Dionysian frenzy—it contains, in thousandfold variation, everything that can stir, destroy and lift up a man's heart again. It is a true microcosm contrasting with the vast universe of this world, an incorruptible and unerring mirror of human existence, in its whole profusion, depth and range of emotions.

[45]

And it is precisely because Beethoven's processes of thought, feeling and experience were deeply bound up with his faith in Man, in Man's inner worth, responsibility and future, that the rich variety in his sense of life could never tempt him to find anything interesting or even noteworthy in all that is negative, questionable, mean or low.

He was not only a great man. He was noble-minded, too.

[46]

In 1802 Beethoven was still, even in outward appearance, a young man. He was short of stature, but powerful and compact. He was bright-eyed and dark-haired; his complexion was wholesome and ruddy; his movements were taut and loaded with energy. Ten years later he was prematurely aged. His hair had gone grey; he was worn-out, heavy and weary. Though he was still capable of fervid outbursts of excitement, rage or enthusiasm, it was only too clear that the radiant vivacity of his youth was lost for ever. And he was still only forty-two years old.

There were always plenty of people—and still are today—who were ready to ascribe this premature decline in a man once blessed with the rudest of health to an immoderate or even depraved mode of life. There have been whispers of Bacchanalian and amorous excesses. No charge could be more foolish or unscrupulous. The material labour alone accomplished by Beethoven in that ten-year period must preclude any reasonable person from seeking the cause of his decline in anything but his colossal physical exertion. But unfortunately there will always be people who take pleasure in 'sullying all that is radiant and dragging what is noble in the dust', so I am going to state the case quite bluntly.

As long as he lived Beethoven enjoyed his glass of wine to the full and, bachelor that he was, he was never a despiser of women. But it is sheer mockery of the truth to impute even occasional acts of debauchery to him. He had neither the time nor the inclination for such things, and his spiritual tension, his fanatical concentration on the one single goal ahead, was a never-failing regulator in matters affecting the physical side of his life.

If it is necessary to seek any other reasons for his premature decline apart from the prodigal expenditure of energy forced on him by his race with deafness, they may be found in a sphere from which nothing could be further removed than vice. All his life Beethoven much disturbed his friends—and everyone else concerned to see his health preserved for the sake of his genius—by his casual attitude towards health matters. As long as he lived he was one of those fanatics of the mind who regard their bodies as mere machines that have no choice but to perform what is demanded of them. It never dawned on him that even the best machines are bound to be ruined by continuous over-strain. He played fast and loose with his health, yet if anyone found the courage to draw his attention to this and beg him to treat his body more rationally, he would either laugh disdainfully or fly into a rage and call his solicitous friend an importunate and uncomprehending idiot who would do better to mind his own business.

It is known that Beethoven never once came into possession of an apartment that was even passably comfortable. He rented lodgings at random; he changed them at the least provocation; he was frequently occupying two at the same time; and as he became more and more irascible and odd under the stress of his increasing deafness and tremendous mental strain, it was inevitable that he soon became known all over Vienna as an undesirable tenant and that the doors of many houses were barred to him from the outset. He had continual disputes and wrangles with servants and the married couples who looked after his domestic needs. In some cases he found himself involved with thoroughly bad characters who lied to him, robbed him and cheated him; in others he often upset servants by unjust accusations and scenes devoid of all reason. No one endured him for long. Nobody is better acquainted with this side of Beethoven's life than I, for whenever the time came round for one more manservant to be sent packing or simply to run away, it was always myself to whom Beethoven turned to find him a speedy replacement. He tried repeatedly and with varying success to run a household of his own—that is, to have meals served at regular times in his home and generally to lead a steady bourgeois life—but in the long run such experiments never came to anything. He was unable to reconcile himself to any such external tidiness in his life. If a meal were announced while he was at work, it would often remain on the table for hours and spoil. If he had ordered his dinner for six o'clock, he would come home at ten. Thus he fell back on taverns and inns where he could have what food he liked when he liked. It was usually the case after long hours of tenacious work in which he had lost all sense of time—either at home or on endless rambles through the countryside—that he would sit down to table with the appetite of a wolf and thoroughly overload his stomach. He was unreasonable, too, in his choice of dishes and used to combine things which did not in the least agree with each other. When these had upset him, he would promptly blame the 'bad cooking.'

All the time I knew Beethoven he suffered from the disorders which are bound to result from such habits—colics which more often than not were quite severe. On a number of occasions he fell seriously ill and was confined to his bed in a wretched condition for weeks on end. Even though he anxiously followed the doctors' instructions to begin with in order to get well again, he just as quickly disregarded their warnings as soon as he felt in the least restored, and went back to his ruinous habits once more. There can be no doubt, I fear, that the serious liver ailment which was finally the death of him was largely due to this folly of his and that it had years in which to get a grip on him.

The same heedlessness marked Beethoven's attitude towards his clothes. Hardly ever paying any attention to the weather, he used to come home soaked to the skin and then sit down at his desk without changing. From time to time he bought new linen or odd items of clothing and assumed in doing so that he was freed of all worry about his appearance for several years to come—until it dawned on him that he was once again presenting himself to his fellow beings in a manner hardly compatible with even the lowest standard of social decency. At home he normally moved about in shirt and trousers and an ancient, tattered dressing-gown which was usually extremely dirty. When he shaved, which was seldom, he did so with such impatience that he spent more time treating his cuts than on the shave itself. His tables, chairs, cupboards and piano groaned under piles of manuscripts and printed scores, so that there was generally no place for visitors to sit except on an occasional chair which was no longer equal to the weight of stacks of music and books.

I should be a dishonest historian were I to suppress or gloss over these facts. They belong to the picture of Beethoven's personality. Ultimately their sum effect is merely to prove what is most important of all in a correct appraisal of his personality: the exclusive and sublime pre-occupation of both musician and man with his spiritual and creative mission.

[47]

Most people who came into contact with Beethoven—among them many who came from far-away places to tender their esteem and veneration—did, in fact, show the right appreciation and understanding for all these things. Admittedly not a few were grieved by the unhappy circumstances of his daily existence, but they sensed with awe that these arose from the extraordinary exigencies of an extraordinary life governed by a lofty moral compulsion. On the other hand it was inevitable that shallow, petty and malicious spirits tried to stamp the artist who lived under such conditions as a simpleton and, unmoved by the grandeur and depth of his work, combed it for traces of the lunacy they thought they had found in its composer.

It would be wrong to suppose that Beethoven himself was distressed by such mean and pitiable stupidity. His weapon in such cases was a legendary coarseness about which at times there was something quite frenzied. Whenever I was present at such outbursts I rejoiced to the very bottom of my soul. To many men there was no other means of bringing home the force of his personality.

[48]

It would also be wrong, moreover, to suppose that Beethoven suffered under these unfortunate and—from the bourgeois point of view—chaotic living conditions. He did not. Most of the time he never even noticed them. All he asked of life 'outside' was not to disturb or interfere with him—a wish he shared with everyone who has ever been under the spell of an engrossing creative task that calls for all one's resources.

There are two conceivable ways, relatively speaking, of satisfying this wish to be left as undisturbed as possible by the demands of the material, bourgeois existence 'outside'. One is to be found in pedantic orderliness and regularity, the other in the utmost disorder and irregularity; one in painstaking observance of all the rules of reason and conventional decorum, the other in total and contemptuous neglect of them. Which way to choose is ultimately a question of individual temperament—though I must confess that I can hardly imagine a musician, of all people, for whom the other alternative of orderliness and regularity could have any appeal.

For the rest, one may consider it extremely fortunate that for all his neglect of bodily welfare and the bourgeois conventions of life, Beethoven had two habits, two tendencies, two dispositional qualities which were particularly fitted to counteract the evil effects of a mode of life that drove his body so relentlessly—qualities which, I am firmly convinced, were actually conducive to the preservation of life and formed the physical source of his energy. I refer first to his habit of spending several hours daily in the open air—mostly on long, hard tramps—and to the closely related fact that he always enjoyed a deep, dreamless sleep that refreshed him like a child. During the wintry half of the year he was to be seen daily on the city bastions, striding out with tireless vigour against the wind and rain; and for the fine months of the year, from May till often well into November, he invariably repaired to the countryside, staying in one of the pretty little towns and villages around Vienna. Out there he has been known, in the fine weather, to remain away from home for whole days and nights, rambling through field and forest and enjoying a few hours' sleep in the open whenever he felt the need of it. His Sixth Symphony, the Pastoral, shows the depth of relaxation and peace which he found in his communion with the forces of living Nature, the rest and recreation without which he could not have met the demands of his creative exertions for so long.

[49]

Just as I was referring above to the other way whereby men working at high pressure are able to erect an insurmountable wall between their innermost selves and the crude, obtrusive, uncomprehending world outside, the memory of another man sprang to my mind—with such force, indeed, that I cannot shake it off. And because, as a modest seeker after truth, I have no interest in making what I write a work of literary art, I am not going to suppress this memory. To my own knowledge it has an intimate bearing on the subject of my narrative, and for me that is sufficient reason for risking the chronological leap which it demands.

I have not only made Goethe's acquaintance through his works; I twice met him personally. Though nothing could be further from my thoughts than to claim that my contact with him was a fruitful one or, as far as he was concerned, even worth recording, both encounters—one in Carlsbad, the other in Marienbad—were for me, nevertheless, of great significance. Experience has taught me that certain very important impressions gained from contact with the human, personal side of great men cannot be replaced by a knowledge, however thorough, of their work or attainments. The fact is that great men have an atmosphere, an aura, about them which exerts a considerable influence on everyone who comes near it.

A sharper contrast than that existing between Goethe and Beethoven I cannot imagine. Goethe was in every way—being just as representative of his type as Beethoven was of his own—one of those great minds who in their everyday pattern of life, clothing, social usages and human relationships meticulously avoid anything that could attract attention or overstep the bounds of popular convention. I believe they do so simply—or at least principally—because they thereby preserve their inner freedom and enclose their own productive, sacred, secret ego from the obtrusive gaze and inquisitiveness of ordinary men and women.

This contrast in their ways of living did in fact prove unbridgeable when Beethoven and Goethe met. This was so not only in the sense that their exchange of ideas turned out unproductive and failed to generate any human warmth, but more than anything else in the sense that Goethe did not perceive Beethoven's greatness as an artist and a man. I was not present when the two men met in the

Bohemian spas in 1812, but everything I heard, not least from Beethoven himself, leaves me in no doubt as to how unpleasant, and at times even painful, this tentative meeting turned out to be. I know that Beethoven's disappointment at Goethe's lack of discernment was lasting and deep.

'I imagined it would be so easy,' Beethoven told me—not on his return from Teplitz but many years later, when I had met Goethe myself and was telling Beethoven about it. 'I thought to myself: so there's the man everyone admires, the great poetic genius—and I thought then that perhaps I wasn't a nonentity either. When someone had achieved what I had, I thought, this man couldn't help recognising a brother at first sight—recognising him as the man closest of all to him, far closer than all the kings, princes, counts and barons of whom Teplitz was so full in those days that you had to be careful you didn't tread on one. . . . I expected him to tell all the princes, counts and barons: "Beethoven, my friend and brother, is here now. You must all step to one side until I've time for you. . . ." That's how Schiller would have treated me if he'd still been alive. Nor would I have had the same wretched dread of Schiller that I had of this man, with his haughty airs, his precise manners, his title of "Excellency" and his bowing and scraping before everything with a crown on its head. . . . In everything he said and did he let me feel that it was all very well to be called Beethoven but that it needn't put any grand ideas in my head. And then I stood there wondering what point there was in being Beethoven at all if the man I considered my equal didn't even notice. . . . I took a long time to get over it. It hurt me, terribly.'

A little later he added:

'I don't believe he understands anything about music. He simply doesn't like to admit it. That's why he always lets old Zelter tell him what to think and say where music is concerned. Old Zelter came to see me recently. He treated me politely enough for the deaf man that I am. But he really doesn't understand anything about music. He's a clumsy oaf.'

Disrespectful remarks are not to my taste. But I am inclined to believe that Beethoven was not entirely wrong when, so late in life, he accused the poet of trying to hide how scanty his understanding of music was. This, too, belonged to Goethe's aura, to his way of living. Had the Eroica been written thirty years earlier, had the youthful genius who wrote *Götz von Berlichingen* been able to hear it, then things might have turned out very differently.

I cannot say whether this is true, but I have it on the creditable authority of our envoy to the Court of Weimar that Goethe not only did not understand Schubert's 'Erlkönig': he actually condemned it. And yet nothing convinced Beethoven quite so much of Schubert's talent as that one composition. He loved Schubert's genius for that song.

[50]

Ο ΜΗ ΔΑΡΕΙΣ ΑΝΘΡΩΠΟΣ ΟΥ ΠΑΙΔΕΥΕΤΑΙ is the motto over Goethe's *Dichtung und Wahrheit*. Beethoven once asked me what it meant. The rendering I gave him was: The man who has not known sorrow is not fully grown.

'And very true!' cried Beethoven. 'Only—he didn't understand *my* sorrow. . . .'

[51]

SOMETHING else occurred between Goethe and Beethoven, however, and the memory of this incident is such a thorn in my flesh that for a time I toyed with the idea of suppressing it lest I became an unjust and biased chronicler. On mature reflection, however, I decided that a chronicler in search of the truth can hardly go to the length of putting himself and his personal reactions entirely to one side. After all, had Beethoven not been so close to my heart, I might never have taken up my pen. I shall, nevertheless, endeavour to express myself quite factually so that the reader may judge for himself whether I am right or wrong in feeling grieved at the incident I now put before him.

Frequently, in the last years of his life, Beethoven found himself financially embarrassed. Why this arose is not the point here and will be dealt with in another connection. At all events Beethoven had to take care to dispose of the few works he produced as profitably as possible; and when he finished the Missa Solemnis he realised that he could hardly expect any success with a work of this nature if he adhered to the normal practice of selling it to a publisher. From such an enormous score as this no publisher could hope to make the profits which would justify his paying a large honorarium to the composer. Then Beethoven had the idea of having the Missa transcribed by copyists and offered to the ruling heads of Europe for their libraries at the connoisseur's price of 50 ducats. Naturally he addressed himself primarily to monarchs to whom he had been presented in the winter of the Great Congress and who at the time had not failed to do homage to his genius. The idea was quite a successful one. Ten or twelve sovereigns responded to the proposal, and after deduction of the copyists' fees Beethoven was left with quite a pretty sum.

Among the monarchs he approached was Karl August,

Grand Duke of Saxe-Weimar, Goethe's eminent friend and patron. And one day I received a message asking me to call on Beethoven. He had not conducted the correspondence with those monarchs personally but through their diplomatic respresentatives in Vienna—a matter in which I was able to help him considerably. Now, however, he was thinking of writing a private letter to Goethe, whose acquaintance he had made twelve years before, to request his good offices with the Grand Duke of Saxe-Weimar. He wanted my advice on how to handle the matter.

'He doesn't like me,' he said. 'I'm sure of that. I brushed him up the wrong way with a vengeance, that time in Teplitz. Perhaps he'll just think me importunate and rude if I write to him. Perhaps I shall do myself more harm than good by asking his help. What do you think?'

I remember what I wrote down in reply as if it had been yesterday:

'Write! Write, whatever you do! Write quite freely what's in your heart. 'Twould be the deuce of a fine thing if the Beethovens of this world were frightened to ask personal favours of the Goethes!'

Beethoven perused what I had written and slowly handed my notebook back to me. He did not appear entirely convinced.

'The world's an odd place . . .' he mused. 'I've known your "deuce of a thing" to happen before now. . . .'

And after brief reflection:

'But I'll do what you say. I'll write. I only ask one thing: read my letter through before I send it off. He's so damned high and mighty with his titles of Privy Counsellor and Excellency that I'm afraid I may upset him with my clumsy language. . . .'

I agreed to do what he asked. Next day Schindler, Beethoven's *adlatus secretarius*, brought me his master's letter, still unsealed, with the request that if I approved I should address and dispatch it; if not I should throw it on the fire. He, Beethoven, would make no second attempt to write so long a letter in a legible hand. (All his life Beethoven's handwriting was unique in its illegibility, and in his last years every word he wrote was a torment to him.)

I made no copy of that letter, nor have I any record of its general purport, so the reader must take my word for the account I give of it here. Perhaps it will come to light again one day and be made accessible to the public; then it will be possible to verify my statements.

The letter is a heart-rending document. Not a single line, not a single word addressed by Beethoven to anyone else can ever, to my knowledge, have carried such deference, such modesty, such touching meekness. In its whole address it was a unique apology for any aspect of Beethoven's behaviour at that Teplitz meeting which might have hurt or offended Goethe; at the same time its human content was deeply moving and of great beauty. Never did Beethoven so bare his heart to another as he did in this letter.

After I had addressed and posted it, I was suddenly assailed by the fear—a senseless, iniquitous fear, I told myself at the time—that this letter might meet with the fate which did in fact befall it.

It was never answered. And the Grand Duke of Saxe-Weimar did not subscribe to the Missa Solemnis.

[52]

It is more than four months since I wrote those last lines. I have been a very sick man in the meantime and did not expect to get my health back—or rather to get back what passes for health in a man of my age and decrepitude. Nevertheless, I am able to write again and I still have my thoughts and perceptions in order, I might as well admit that for me being 'well' has come to mean being able to carry on with my work on this chronicle and, if possible, to finish it. The desire to achieve this may even have contributed to my recovery—if one may call it that.

After my long and painful illness I was sent to convalesce in Baden. I went with some reluctance. Once so quiet and charming, the little watering place whose springs have been such a frequent boon to me has grown into an extremely fashionable and busy resort. It is, as the saying goes, *en vogue*, and during the Season it becomes the meeting place for the cream of Viennese society. All who wish to 'belong to the right set'—Prince Metternich before anyone else—have built or purchased a house there; the casino has acquired a splendid new hall; hotels and guest-houses are springing up all over the place; and ladies and gentlemen of all classes, from members of the imperial family down to the worst types of adventurer, fill the little town with futile activity. Usurers, procurers and social intriguers who have settled there find lucrative employment. From time to time a duel is fought; now and again a suicide provides a few days' gossip; and whenever there is no political or social sensation to keep people on tenterhooks, someone discovers a few orphans or other unfortunates for whom it is felt necessary to organise a bazaar, masked ball or grand concert, with tombola included.

At my age one finds such things more empty and silly than they really are. But what astonishes and displeases me is this: in the days of Maria Theresa and the Emperor Josef—dear God, how terribly far off they seem now!—we young people also used to enjoy ourselves. We fell in love; we thought it immensely important to know which of us a fair lady would favour; we rode and drove with hand-picked horses as if our eternal salvation depended on how good a figure we cut; we could debate the relative merits of this or that ruffle, hair style, ring, snuff-box or breast-pin for hours at a time; we prattled and gossiped no less than one does today. All this I admit.

But there was one great difference between then and now. We never spoke of money and we did not choose our friends by the size of their purses. Other qualities decided whether one 'belonged' or not. And if I ask myself what these were, I must conclude that they were qualities of the heart—tact, discretion and feeling. Whatever else a man might be—stupid or bright, Vienna dandy or country squire, bashful swain or dashing buck, soldier or scholar—was of secondary importance; and differences of temperament and talent merely served to give variety to life. But anyone who was tactless and insensible to the rule of always letting the 'other' person—be it man or woman—decide the distance to be maintained between two individuals or two groups of people, anyone who was indiscreet and incapable of keeping to himself anything which had accidentally come to his ears, anyone who was indifferent to human misfortune and could muster no enthusiasm for beauty or truth in any form—that man quite definitely did not 'belong', however elevated his birth.

Today, on the other hand—and I see this in a thousand minor details, a thousand different shades of behaviour—the most unprincipled blackguard, the most sordid adventurer, the most shameless egoist can attain a leading position in society if only he is amply provided with what Iago recommended to Cassius as the most important thing in the world.

I am ready to believe that there is no longer a single vice, however abominable, which cannot be made to appear an interesting and endearing foible if there is a sufficiently large fortune behind it.

Whenever I was wheeled through the spa gardens in my invalid's chair, however, I had no grounds for complaint. People would stop for a chat and tell me the latest anecdotes and scandals; and many a pretty, exuberant young woman would spare a radiant smile for my frailty and age. They would ask me about Maria Theresa and the Emperor Josef, about Napoleon and Alexander of Russia, about Prince Rasumovsky, Neipperg and the King of Rome. They would ask me whether I had already heard *Die Diebische Elster* or what I thought of Castelli's latest comedy. They would ask me if I really had worn a wig when I was a page and whether it had given me a headache. They would ask how I liked the latest fashions and whether I did not find them infinitely more becoming than the costumes of the last century. They asked me about everything and everyone. The only name they never mentioned was Beethoven's. I was probably the only person in the whole of Baden to remember that less than ten years before, the Ninth Symphony had come to life here, besides the Diabelli Variations and a great part of the last five string quartets. And when I remembered, I used to rejoice at my growing strength and look forward to my quiet apartment in Vienna. I would think of the piano that had so often rung out under Beethoven's touch, and of the desk containing the manuscript which I might yet still finish.

[53]

Now that I am actually back at that desk again and have re-read what I had written to date in an attempt to retrieve the thread of my narrative, something tells me I have no more time to lose. Henceforth I must confine myself to essentials, even at the risk of ignoring some of the broader aspects of the story.

But first I would beg leave to give a brief explanation of what these essentials imply.

Beethoven's work—and this is something I feel with ever-increasing certainty—must speak for itself, must be its own witness in the decades and centuries ahead of us. Should the present lack of appreciation for his work persist—then all I can do is to pity a world unable to feel moved and enriched by such music. But I fully expect it to go from triumph to triumph and to capture the hearts of all men and women to whom music means anything at all; I fully expect these same men and women, when the man who made that music has for years lain under the earth, to want to know not *what* he was but *who* he was. They will need no help from me to discover *what* he was; but they still want to know *who* he was, what *kind* of man was behind that music, wherein lay the uniqueness of the soul that gave birth to such work—and it is this discovery that I hope to facilitate by these notes.

My illness was at least considerate enough to interrupt the narrative at a point where the nature and substance of my story would have demanded a certain pause. I have done my best to show how Beethoven came to cross the threshold to those ten prolific years of creative achievement so steeped in beauty and feeling. Such an achievement might be called a triumph of Promethean revolt against a blindly relentless Anangke, the victory of Man over misanthropic Fate. I could not attempt more; neither was it my wish to do so.

In covering those ten years of incomparable creative effort, my narrative has necessarily neglected Beethoven the man. The commitment to which he pledged himself in the year 1802 reigned supreme throughout that period, and no major changes took place in his spiritual landscape.

But when those ten years were over, a landslide occurred in Beethoven's soul—a cataclysm which entirely reshaped its familiar contours. It did not occur—and this is the whole point—in the sense that a long-expected total deafness now put an end to his composing and condemned the artist in him to ultimate silence; on the contrary, the new spiritual landscape created by the destruction of the first turned out, to Beethoven's own deep surprise and delight, to be fertile soil for a musical work, new both in form and in content, which I rate at least as high as—in one respect even higher than—the Promethean work of the preceding ten years.

This fact, which borders on the miraculous, is to determine the future course of my narrative.

Had things turned out as Beethoven expected throughout the ten years of his race with deafness, had that period of creative endeavour ended with his having to lay down his pen and spend his remaining years in idleness, any attempt to depict his spiritual landscape towards the end of his life would have resulted in a document which, though perhaps intensely saddening, could only have been of negative significance. Had things turned out that way, I would never have attempted the task. And resolved though I was, in the event of the musician's being finally silenced, to prove to the afflicted soul who remained—to prove by doubled, yes, tenfold friendship, solicitude and affection—how very much I esteemed and revered him—if it had actually come to that, I should have no reason today for setting out on my own hectic race with the Fate that menaces me or for pressing on with this chronicle as Death peers over my shoulder.

I will, I must, still find time to conduct my readers through the cataclysm of the years 1812–16 into the landscape of the last ten or eleven years of Beethoven's life—my inner urge to do so being intensified all the more by the knowledge that I am the last living witness of those happenings. Certainly there is no other person alive today who was affected by them deeply enough to recognise their importance.

[54]

I HAVE heard it so often now that I no longer have any illusions on the subject: most people, including many with a special love for the works produced in what I call Beethoven's Promethean period, think little or nothing of the few compositions he produced in his last years. They choose to regard them as abstruse and confused experiments, as the meaningless fantasies of a musical brain stamped with the tragic incapacity of deafness. People have assured me, whenever I objected to such assertions, that Beethoven himself would have stopped his ears had he miraculously been given the power to hear these products of his last years. Admittedly, they say, the Missa and the Ninth Symphony contain passages of sublime beauty, but no one with normal powers of apprehension in the face of such things as the Piano Sonata Opus 106, the second movement of the Sonata Opus 111, the Diabelli Variations or, most of all, the last five string quartets, can close his eyes to the fact that these are the painful, melancholy monstrosities of a doomed genius—in a word, that these things should be suppressed and destroyed.

And that, I may say, is the milder of the two attitudes I am accustomed to encounter. Those of the present generation who are left unmoved even by Beethoven's early work—they are the same people who find Rossini 'divine' and wildly applaud the virtuoso pianists of the day—laugh in one's face at the very mention of Beethoven's later works and have no hesitation in dismissing them out of hand as the products of a sick brain. They go on to claim, moreover, that even in his earlier works one may detect signs of incipient madness—madness which in their view would have declared itself in any case, deafness or no deafness. . . .

I am not contesting either of these views. Should they persist, should later generations be unable to discover the world of beauty and understanding that these works contain for me and a few others, should these works really remain—as most people maintain they will—a book with seven seals which no normal mind can break—well, in that case I will gladly admit to having been a fool, a dreamer, an undiscriminating simpleton who discovered pearls where none existed. I am not writing—nor did I write any of the foregoing—for people to whom these last works of Beethoven's convey nothing. I shall be quite content if they push this little book contemptuously aside, if in their own shallow minds they bury the fool Zmeskall next to the fool Beethoven. I would feel infinitely happier in the company of the fool Beethoven than in the company of the people who thought him a fool.

And now I will try to tell what I know and what seems to me to be of relevance.

[55]

BEETHOVEN's life was full of contretemps, irritations and annoyances, not least in the years of his incessant creative struggle. When a man is in the habit of carrying three or four different works around in his head simultaneously, polishing and varying these even as new ones wait impatiently on the threshold of his consciousness, it is not to be wondered at if he finds little sympathy or tolerance for the realities and more comfortable pace of everyday life or for the petty irritations of mere persons and things. None the less, there are two kinds of annoyance: that which, as I have just pointed out, is part of the normal state of a man exposed to extreme mental strain; and that which is significant not only for its acuteness but also because a certain something about it reveals it to be a warning signal, the forerunner of an impending crisis. Indeed, it may well be because it heralds some profound upheaval that this latter kind of annoyance inflicts such gashes.

As an arbitrator and mediator I had quite enough to do with the offences given or suffered by Beethoven not to be unduly worried by them when they occurred. The very nature of our friendship made me the obvious man for that office—and I took pains to perform it in such a way that I remained a mediator, in the eyes both of Beethoven and of other people.

I first noticed that something was going seriously wrong, that something alarming was beginning to affect Beethoven's attitude to the worries and hazards of everyday life, by the way he reacted to the difficulties and inconveniences arising from the notorious Finance Decree of spring 1811. Since people wrote, argued, ranted and raved quite enough about this at the time, it will probably suffice to recall that its effect was to render everyone who was dependent on a fixed income for his livelihood two-thirds poorer than before. For such was the ratio of the currency devaluation which followed the Decree—to say nothing of the rise in the actual cost of living, which had been going up steadily for some considerable time. Now Beethoven's income, too, was in part a 'fixed' income—namely the part of it deriving from the payments of these three eminent gentlemen who had settled a pension of 6,000 florins a year on him. Consequently a certain readjustment of this pension became necessary if it was still to fulfil its purpose of guaranteeing Beethoven an existence free of economic worry. And although his three patrons were not lacking in understanding or goodwill—despite being themselves hard hit by the general impoverishment of which the Decree was merely the outcome—things like this naturally took a certain time, and it can well be imagined that their respective financial advisers were initially pre-occupied with far more urgent affairs than the problem of deciding how Beethoven's annuity from the endowment of 1809 should in future be arranged.

In due course the matter was settled in a manner which does great honour to Beethoven's patrons—but not before Beethoven had taken offence in a fashion that was exaggerated from both the material and the emotional point of view. He quite openly accused his patrons of seeking to 'defraud' him and to make an improper and dishonourable profit from the Finance Decree—thereby entirely overlooking the fact that, legally speaking, his patrons were under no obligation to adjust his annuity to the new, devalued currency. He further overlooked the fact that many hundreds of thousands of Austrians had been incomparably harder hit by the Finance Decree than he, since a large part of his means were the proceeds of his compositions, and these proceeds had not only been rising steadily for years past but were also paid out in precious foreign currencies. When the point was reached where Beethoven actually allowed an extremely dubious lawyer to talk him into instituting legal proceedings against the one of his three patrons whom he considered especially dilatory—a most questionable act in the moral sense, quite apart from the fact that it had no prospects of succeeding in court—I realised that the sense of injury which was obviously at the bottom of all his indignation and anger was far exceeding the proportions one had come to regard as normal, and I began to feel gravely concerned about his mental equilibrium. As for the lawsuit he had initiated, I and other level-headed advisers were soon able to talk him out of it, and when the patron involved met a sudden and accidental death while still in the prime of life, we did not take long to persuade Beethoven to adopt a reasonable attitude towards the widow and heir. As I have said, the affair in itself was finally settled in a most satisfactory and even generous manner.

That was the first thing to put me on my guard and prepare me inwardly for the impending storm.

The second was as follows. While hurrying across the

street one day I was stopped by the doctor then attending Beethoven—a well-known and popular physician.

'A word in your ear,' he said. 'It's about Beethoven. . . .'

'*Du lieber Gott!* I trust it's not bad news? Has he sent for you?'

'Yes,' the other told me. 'Violent stomach pains once again—and very serious, too. But that's not why I wanted to talk to you—we shall soon be over it provided he shows a little sense. No, what struck me as so strange—and considerably embarrassed me, too—was something else. I thought it my duty to point out that he really must think seriously about taking a long rest and a proper cure; I tried to make him see that he's no longer at the age when one can play fast and loose with one's constitution, and that he'd be well advised to economise his strength a little. You know yourself he's no longer young for his forty-two years.

'Well, he listened to me quite coolly, and when I'd finished my lecture, he asked what I actually envisaged by a "cure."

'I asked what he thought of six or eight weeks at one of the Bohemian spas. Teplitz or Carlsbad could work wonders . . . quite apart from being popular places where he would find stimulating and excellent company. . . .

'He looked at me in a way that was half crafty and half angry—and then out it all came. . . . Did I fancy he was one of the Frankfurt Rothschilds? Where was he, a poor musician, to raise the money to fiddle away his time in the most expensive and fashionable spas? Hadn't I noticed what bad times we were living in? To cut a long story short, a furious storm beat down on my head and I slunk away quite disconcerted.

'But tell me, Zmeskall, have I really committed a *faux pas*? I always thought he was quite comfortably off. In any case, surely one can exist on a relatively modest footing even in places like Teplitz and Carlsbad? I had the best of intentions—he does badly need the waters. . . .'

I pacified the doctor as best I could. I told him that Beethoven had probably been more deeply affected by the gravity of his professional opinion that he cared to admit—this was simply the way he was made—and that he had found it convenient to plead financial stringency and turn aggressive in order to hide his real disquiet. . . . I assured him that Beethoven was not at all badly off financially and and that I hoped to persuade him to take the physician's advice. And with that we parted.

On the afternoon of the same day I went to see Beethoven. He was lying in bed surrounded by medicine bottles, and in the best of moods.

'Hallo, *Musikgraf*!' he welcomed me, smiling broadly. 'I'm going to mix with dandies and high society. Dr M. has prescribed me Teplitz and Carlsbad! Now I shall bathe and rinse my precious body out with the same waters that are privileged to trickle over and percolate through the sacred bellies of kings, princes and counts . . .'

(It was already known that this very year a number of European monarchs and their ministers were to meet—some officially and others incognito—in the Bohemian spas. Napoleon's campaign against Russia was imminent, and anti-Napoleonic Europe scented new opportunities.)

He went on cracking wilder and wilder jokes and sketching increasingly grotesque pictures of the rôle he proposed to play that summer as a member of the most select society on earth—how he would flabbergast them all with his elegant clothes and impeccable manners.

'Dear me,' he mocked, 'His Imperial Majesty's Aulic Councillor seems surprised to see what a poor, despised composer can rise to! And when I drive into Teplitz with a post-chaise and four—or would you advise me to acquire a carriage of my own?—people will throw open their windows and stare after me and say: "Did you see him, the little fellow with grey hair? That was Beethoven—the great Beethoven from Vienna!" '

And though, when I actually saw him off to Teplitz a few weeks later, I earnestly hoped to find him restored and settled in a few months' time, I hoped against my better knowledge; I hoped in order to drown a quiet, ominous voice inside me. It was a voice of anxiety and dread and it refused to be silenced.

[56]

AM I permitted to tell of it or not? The pros and cons of this question have long exercised my mind. If it had been fourteen years ago I could still have excused my indiscretion, both to myself and to my reader, by the fact that the grave disappointment suffered by Beethoven in his emotional life was—in its broader aspects, at any rate—the common property of all who knew him. Now, however, the position is such that no one, apart from the persons immediately involved, has any knowledge of that intimate and tragic circumstance. What is perhaps even more important is that Beethoven himself never uttered a single word to me about it as long as he lived. On the other hand, I did not come to hear of his misfortune by mere chance but through the touching confidence of the woman concerned. Thus I, too, am one of the people 'immediately involved', and as there are factors here which have the most direct bearing on Beethoven's emotional development—factors without knowledge of which this development cannot be properly understood—my personal connection saddles me with a responsibility which I can hardly evade in view of my pledge to posterity and my own conscience to produce an account in true keeping with my knowledge of the inward course of Beethoven's life. It just would not do, at this critical juncture, simply to tell my reader that we had now come to a matter on which I personally was fully informed and about which it was vital to know in order to have any insight into all that followed—but that unfortunately I was not authorised to discuss it.

Ultimately the question of how discreet or indiscreet a chronicler is must depend on how correctly he assesses the relative values involved. If posterity has a right to be told not merely the truth but the whole truth about Beethoven as a really great man and musician, then I, as one so wholeheartedly convinced of his greatness, have the least right of all to suppress anything vital.

[57]

When I was about forty-five years old I had the fortune, thanks to the good offices of my patron, Count Palffy, to be introduced to a family of the upper nobility with whose many members—parents, children and cousins—I gradually formed close bonds of friendship that have mostly survived up to the present day. The people in question were a married couple in the best of circumstances who had decided, mainly for the sake of their two lovely daughters, to give up their fine country seat to settle in Vienna. They rented a roomy, well-appointed house which they furnished with taste and every comfort; and Viennese society showed itself highly delighted with the new arrivals. Since people felt at home with them, a brisk social round developed; and it did not take long for the family to be accepted as fully fledged and popular members of their new milieu.

Among other things they took a warm and serious interest in music, if not in the same spectacular fashion as the Lichnowskis and Lobkowitzes, and it was I who introduced Beethoven into the family. Because of the way he inspired everyone who had any understanding of music, he was received with open arms and quickly won the respect and friendships of the parents.

I myself soon realised that something other than friendship was drawing me to that household. The elder of the two daughters—I will call her Astarte—had greatly impressed me from the outset, and the closer our acquaintance became, the more deeply I was convinced of her quite exceptional worth. She could not be called provocatively beautiful—which her younger sister undoubtedly was. Nevertheless, she was tall and slim and possessed qualities which in my eyes make a woman even more attractive than beauty: a captivating charm and simple warmth deriving from an inexhaustible and quite spontaneous kindness of heart. Her intelligence and high degree of culture, her sincere enthusiasm for everything pure and fine, in no way obtruded on people's attention, and it almost amused me to see what rapturous homage everyone paid to the really fascinating younger sister while virtually ignoring the nobility of the elder.

About a year after meeting the family, I resolved to lay bare my feelings to the girl I adored, for I was convinced I could never make a better choice. Cautious inquiries on my part had already met with the friendly encouragement of her parents, despite the considerable discrepancy in age between Astarte and myself. Probably they felt that Astarte's whole personality fitted her better for a mature man than for some young buck unable to appreciate her true worth.

I called on my beloved on an afternoon when I knew she would be alone, and with profound emotion presented my suit. She had hardly understood what I sought of her before I saw what a mistake I had made. Perplexity and genuine distress clouded her features as she gently withdrew the hand that I had seized. And then, her dark eyes filling with tears, she softly explained why she could not be mine.

She was in love. She loved someone else with the whole intensity of her soul. She loved Beethoven.

Painful and crushing though her admission was to me, I know that my heart remained untouched by any mean pang of jealousy. I know, too, that she sensed this with an intimate conviction. She had entrusted me with the secret of her own heart, she had paid me the honour of telling the truth about herself, and because I did not disappoint her and showed myself deserving of this honour we were able to salve our deep friendship from the wreckage of my hopes. In order to ease her own position, I promised not to shun her or her family, for her love was obviously so hopeless, in the worldly and social sense, that any revelation of the reasons why she had refused me was bound to have the worst possible consequences for both herself and Beethoven. To obviate all danger of this we resolved to act as if my proposal had never been made. I later told Astarte's mother that I had after all been unable to make up my mind to accept responsibility at my time of life for the happiness of a girl so much younger than myself; as the mother knew how deeply I loved Astarte, she assumed that this was merely the story I was telling to cover up my own defeat. She did not press me for details, but by redoubled kindness helped me to foster the impression that no idea of my marrying her daughter had ever seriously existed.

Whether at that stage there was already a conscious and explicit understanding between Astarte and Beethoven, I was unable to tell. I was inclined to doubt it. I even doubted whether Beethoven so much as guessed what feelings that adorable young girl cherished for him in her heart. As I have said, a union between Astarte and Beethoven was a sheer impossibility, and the girl could not seriously contemplate trying to enlist her parents' and sister's support. Had she, in such circumstances, an interest in encouraging her loved one to make any advances? Was she not much surer of continuing to enjoy his company and proximity if no one suspected what was going on within her? And might it not have jeopardised everything if she had allowed such a fanatic for straightforwardness as Beethoven to suspect the truth?

Besides, love of the deep, enthralling kind that Astarte felt for Beethoven has something clairvoyant about it. She may well have sensed what was going on in the man she loved. She was sensitive enough to perceive the coat of mail he had forged round his heart to isolate it from all human contact—sensitive enough to feel that in the soul of her loved one a struggle was raging around momentous issues whose success could be endangered by any emotional crisis. She probably guessed that by giving way to the desires of her own heart—at the present juncture, at least—she might do the man she loved more harm than good and bring confusion into a soul needing all its energies to attain its paramount aim—the fulfilment of its creative mission.

I do not know when or how this latent state of affairs came to an end. I only know that I never doubted that Beethoven's heart must burst into flame the moment he realised Astarte's feelings for him. And the later he made this discovery, the deeper its impression on him would be. For here indeed, tested through years of silent loyalty, was what he had longed for all his life: the woman's heart that belonged to him, beat and lived for him *because* he was Beethoven, because he was the artist whose duty it was to be Beethoven. Here glowed the love that was destined for him alone, just as he was and always must be.

I am sure, too, that Astarte had never told him anything of my proposal of marriage or that she had confided the secret of her heart to me. Otherwise, what now came to pass in the summer of 1812 could never have been.

[58]

THAT summer, in view of the extremely tense position in the field of foreign affairs, I had received no leave. Count Palffy, though in Budapest, was not resting either, and he attached great importance to having a reliable representative and informant in Vienna during his absence. It had been very hot in July and August—or so it seemed to me, unaccustomed as I was to city life in summertime—and when September brought the first cool days, I frequently made little excursions into the surrounding countryside. One morning, returning from a ride of several hours' duration, I found Astarte waiting for me in my apartment.

As some quite exceptional occurrence must have caused her to take this surprising step, and in order not to keep her waiting any longer, I put off changing my clothes and greeted her hot and dusty as I was. Paying no heed to my apologies, she clung imploringly to my hand and gasped:

'Where is Beethoven? I beg you—tell me where he is!'

'*Verehrte und liebe Freundin*, what has happened? How comes it that you ask me . . . ?'

'Nikolaus—I beseech you, where is Beethoven? I've been out of touch with him for over two months. I *must* know where he is and how I can reach him. . . .'

'Out of touch with him for over two months? Astarte, you frighten me . . . How can that be?' But her gaze held mine: she still sought the answer to her question. 'I'm not sure where he is, but it can't be difficult to find him. He was to stay at the spas till about this time, and then he meant to go to Linz to see his brother. We should expect him back here early in October.'

This vague information, which was the best I could give, seemed too much for Astarte in her present high-strung condition. She dropped into an armchair and burst into a fit of weeping which was pathetic to see.

How shall I describe the poor child's distress? I felt for

her most deeply and did my utmost to pacify her in her torment. Again and again, in words of deep emotion, I promised her my every assistance and asked her to tell me what form this might take.

Then, her tears stilled, she looked up and said: 'How good it is to have a friend. . . .'

What, then, had happened? Was it really as bad as all that? Perhaps I could advise her?

And then she began her story. Not in the way I reproduce it here, but haltingly and frequently interrupted by fresh fits of weeping. This is what I learnt:

Without Astarte's knowing how it happened, without any conscious move on her part to bring it about, Beethoven had a few months previously made the discovery which she yearned for and feared in equal measure. It may be that he had long known of her love but had deliberately refrained from surrendering to the feelings it evoked. At all events, one day they had fallen speechlessly into each other's arms and plighted their most sacred and binding troth. The weeks and months which followed had been a heaven on earth for both of them. On one point only did they fail to agree: Beethoven wanted to approach Astarte's father quite openly and ask for her hand; he could not comprehend her fear of such a step. In his ecstasy, in his blissful possession of the riches with which Astarte's heart had presented him, he overlooked all the objections that her father would raise against such a union; he did not and would not grasp that anyone could be so criminally unreasonable as to want to prevent the alliance of two human beings brought together by God. Astarte, for her own part, expected the worst from her parents, dreading the pain of her mother even more than the wrath of her father, and fought to keep her secret, the very substance of which, her intuition told her, disclosure would destroy. Nevertheless, her lover remained adamant. Astarte sensed that he was moved here by a moral conviction of such depth that not even her whole love, not even her whole knowledge of human nature and the world, could induce him to accept her own judicious outlook and bow to her wish. So she gave way. It was agreed that some time in July Beethoven would take advantage of his own sojourn in the Bohemian spas to come to Carlsbad, where Astarte would be staying with her parents, to make the decisive *démarche*.

And then, during this phase of anxiety and suspense in which Astarte awaited the impending *dénouement* with an uneasy yet exultant heart, something had happened which defies description. Was it a cruel trick of fate or was it a trivial coincidence? It really had something of both of these—it was one of those happenings which reduce a man to hopeless perplexity by the way they show up the most vital and sacred things in a petty, ridiculous light and force him to fight a decisive battle on a plane he finds alien and unworthy. In short, Astarte's father had come into possession of a letter sent to her in Carlsbad by her lover: he had broken it open and read the contents. . . .

It had not even remotely occurred to him what depth and intensity of feeling, what ardour, what supreme human experience his daughter's love involved. He regarded this love as nothing more than an undignified and shameful aberration, an incomprehensible disgrace which at once cut him to the quick and incurred his utmost wrath. Knowing Astarte's father, I could picture the frigid severity and resolve with which he took his counter-measures: knowing him, I could understand that Astarte, her will paralysed and incapable of opposition, had to comply with what he demanded of her. She was compelled to return her lover's letter to him unread and in an envelope addressed in her own hand, with not a line, not a single word of explanation—all this in the presence of the father who pressed the pen into her hand. Thereafter she was put under such close surveillance that she found no means of communicating with Beethoven by letter or messenger.

'I knew it was the end,' said Astarte. 'In his cruelty Father had unerringly picked out the softest spot in Beethoven's character—his pride. To have his own letter sent back to him in that way—that was something he would never understand and never forgive—it would destroy him. . . . I trembled and fretted with fear and dread . . . I feared the worst. . . .'

'Astarte!' I cried in a surge of anger, pity and indignation, 'it can't have ended that way! That cannot—that must not be!'

An expression of indescribable sorrow passed over her features.

'No,' she said, 'it didn't end that way. . . . After I had tormented myself in silence for two weeks or so, with no one to understand or console me, closely guarded and forced to hide my grief from all the people we met, received and visited, my parents must have decided I was beginning to "see reason" . . . and one afternoon I managed to escape unobserved from the house we occupied. All I wanted was to be alone with my thoughts, to come to myself and shake off the nightmare that was oppressing me and to find my own soul again. . . . So I went out into the open country where I should not meet a familiar face at every turn—and suddenly he stood before me. . . .'

'Beethoven?' I cried.

'Yes, it was Ludwig. He took me in his arms and pressed me tenderly to him—more like a father than a lover—and whispered: "My poor, poor child—what have they done to you. . . ."'

Astarte began to sob once more, overwhelmed by her memory of the scene. In silence I waited for what would follow.

When his letter was so disdainfully returned to him, Beethoven had immediately guessed what was wrong. Not for a moment had he lost faith in the woman he loved, his one and only thought being to gain access to her without the knowledge of her sentinels. In this he had shown so much shrewdness and circumspection that he had now actually succeeded, on the first occasion Astarte was out unaccompanied, in coming face to face with her again and giving her proof of his faith, understanding and love.

'I don't believe,' said Astarte, 'that any woman has ever been raised so swiftly from utter despair, dread and sorrow into a paradise of happiness—and I don't believe that what I still have to tell could have happened had I not been so absurdly happy, so far removed from this world of reality and so oblivious of my actual position. . . .

'Ludwig thought of it, though. And probably he was right. But I didn't understand him. I was exhausted by everything I had gone through. I wished only for peace and security, I longed only to forget that there was any other reality but that of being in Ludwig's arms, in the protection of his love and fidelity. . . .

'I must go away with him now, that very minute, Beethoven urged. I must go just as I was—hatless, gloveless and in my light summer dress. Anything else was hopeless; each minute's delay could be the end of everything. My absence was bound to have been noticed already; they would come after me; and if they found me here, they would tear me from his arms for ever and send me far away; I should be guarded so closely that he would never find the way to me again.

'He implored me, he spoke with the tongues of angels, he became almost wild with frustration when at first I didn't understand what he wanted of me and then, having understood, couldn't summon up the sense or courage to follow him. . . .

'Oh, Nikolaus!' Astarte cried out in her anguish, 'what a wretched creature I am! In the *one* decisive moment of my life, I failed! I thought of the distress of my parents; I thought of all the things that would be said about me. I thought people would point at me in the street; I thought of the way Carlsbad would echo for weeks to come with the story of my flight; I thought of my brothers and sister; I recalled that not even the shadow of a scandal had ever passed over our name.

'The longer, the more passionately Ludwig insisted, the more my heart contracted within me. Finally I threw myself down on a stone seat under an image of the Virgin, hid my head in my arms and moaned "I can't—I can't—I can't. . . ."

'When I looked up again, Ludwig was no longer there. I could see him, already out of range of my cries, walking back towards the town with firm, angry strides. . . . His feet stamped up tiny clouds of dust. . . . I can't explain why, but as I saw him disappearing into the distance, hands clenched behind his back, stubborn head thrown back, I knew . . . that . . . that this time . . . it really *was* all over. . . .'

Astarte's eyes, by now drained of all expression, met my own. I was silent, deeply shocked by the picture she had conjured up in my mind—the picture of a man, shattered in his most sacred trust, leaving the scene of his cruellest defeat to set grimly forth on his journey towards the last, bleakest solitude of all.

Then Astarte suddenly jumped to her feet and stretched out her hands to me in a gesture of entreaty:

'It *can't* be over—it *mustn't* be over!' she pleaded. 'Nikolaus, if you have ever loved me—help me, help me to find Beethoven! Help me to make him understand that I only acted as I did from sheer weariness and passing weakness! Help me to make him see that he can't demand too much at once from so frail a girl! Help me to win back his trust! Tell him how fully I now realise how I hurt him—tell him that in two months of despair I've learnt to curse that weakness of mine and that I shall never fail him again! Tell him I'm ready to come straight to him at any hour of the day or night, that I'm not afraid of anything any more, that I'm ready to shout it into the face of the world that I shall love him, and him alone, as long as my heart goes on beating! Tell him he can believe and trust in this heart from now on—more than anything else in the world! Oh, Nikolaus, you are his friend—he'll listen to you! Help me! I beseech you, help me!'

Sobbing bitterly, she threw herself into my arms. As I stroked her hair, I said with deep sorrow in my heart:

'You love Beethoven, Astarte—but you don't *know* him. He never forgives. To him forgiveness means accepting something imperfect. He's never learnt to do that and he never will.'

A few days later I heard that Beethoven was indeed in Linz, at his brother's home. I told Astarte. She wrote him a long letter in which she poured out her heart. Then he did the same thing as had been done to him: he returned her letter unopened.

[59]

NEVER had Beethoven put my friendship to a harder test. Indeed, I think he was the only man who could have behaved like that without losing it. Once again, it had to be seen in a wider perspective. Only the man who had been so ruthless with himself could be permitted to treat a fellow being so ruthlessly. More than that, he *had* to act in that way. But this—the fact that he had acted under compulsion—did not dawn on me till much later—that is, not until he had overcome the crisis he was now entering and had started on his new, late work. It will be understood in due course what I mean. At this stage I will say no more than this: had he not been so harsh to Astarte, had he allowed her remorse to soften him, and had he married her, I am quite certain that he would never have accomplished that later work.

Even Astarte came to appreciate this after years of suffering and piteous torment. She had learnt to regard the hour of her weakness and failure, which evoked all the inexorability of Beethoven's nature, as a disposition from above—a disposition of that Power whose desire it was that Beethoven's other, late work should still come into being.

[60]

WHAT I next witnessed, however, on Beethoven's return to Vienna was not a tragedy but a satiric drama.

In Linz there had been sharp clashes between Beethoven and his brother—scenes of such foolishness and naïvety as can only occur between brothers temporarily oblivious of the fact that they have meanwhile become grown-up people.

Beethoven was hardly back from Linz and still very much under the impression of his experiences there when he told me that whole story. It was palpably clear that the violence of his agitation and resentment arose not least from a desire to deaden within himself all recollection of the terrible disappointment he had suffered with Astarte and the terrible decision he had driven himself to make regarding her. It was equally clear that he would never have proceeded with such hot-tempered severity against his brother in Linz if the cruel ending to his love for Astarte had not torn at the very roots of his heart.

The reader will remember that letter of Count Waldstein's many years ago in which he told me about young Beethoven and his family feeling, about his paramount will to protect the honour and good name of that family from disgrace and ruin. This conviction of being responsible for the honour of the family had never left Beethoven: far from growing weaker with the passage of the years, it had determined a whole series of his actions. The reason why I have not come back to it before is that the question of family relations had not, since those early days in Bonn, cast any real shadow on his life; certainly it had not had any decisive influence on the development of the Beethoven who belongs to the world and of whom I am trying to paint a living picture in these lines. What had occurred could even now be safely passed over in silence had Beethoven's brothers confined themselves to the modest and insignificant rôle which they had played to date during Beethoven's years in Vienna. But this they did not do. Henceforth, beginning with the conflict in Linz, they forced themselves more and more to the front of the stage—and this makes it necessary for us to examine them more closely.

[61]

There were two of them. The elder was called Johann, the younger Karl. Johann was an apothecary; Karl was originally a musician and later, when it became clear how little real talent he possessed, a humble municipal official.

Immediately Beethoven had gained a reasonable degree of economic security as a young man, he had fetched both brothers to Vienna—not least, as he often assured me, because he credited neither of them with any great character and wished to 'keep his eye on them'. He supported both of them for many a year; he brought influence and connections to bear—as no one knows better than I—in favour of both of them; and eventually he succeeded, albeit with frequent annoyances and reverses, in providing each with quite an adequate livelihood. So far, so good. But from the outset the thanks he earned were precious small. He made repeated efforts to promote each of the brothers to positions of trust; he even tried to employ the younger one, Karl, as a kind of confidential secretary; but in neither case were the results at all gratifying. They had no respect for him, they considered themselves superior, they interfered in many things which were no concern of theirs, and they grossly abused his trust. This last—I see no reason for concealing it—included money matters. In short, Beethoven had no easy life with his two brothers, and it is a measure of his extraordinarily strong sense of responsibility that he allowed none of these experiences, which were often of a most unpleasant kind, to induce him to take the action that so many of his friends—not least myself—advised: namely to abandon both brothers to their extremely uninteresting fates.

It is Johann, the elder brother, who must concern us first. After working for several years as a dispenser in a Vienna pharmacy, he had succeeded in acquiring a business of his own in Linz. He had not done this with savings of his own, of which he had none, but with money belonging to his elder brother Ludwig, and also by owing the vendor a considerable sum which was to be paid off from the proceeds of the business in yearly instalments agreed by contract. It soon emerged that he had involved himself in much too risky an undertaking, and by 1808 bankruptcy was knocking at his door. Then, however, came the year 1809. The Napoleonic armies overran South Germany; Ulm had fallen; Vienna was threatened and taken, and the battles of Austerlitz and Wagram were lost. For Johann van Beethoven, the apothecary of Linz, all this meant profitable contracts with the French Emperor's quartermaster-general—contracts which not only stabilised his financial position but in very few years even made him well off.

He became more and more pleased with himself in the rôle of a man-about-town, dressing very foppishly and making increasingly frequent journeys in his own carriage to Vienna, where he liked to play the cavalier.

Ludwig found all this rather laughable but—again for reasons of family pride—was pleased at his brother's obvious prosperity. 'There really is something in him after all!' he would say with a knowing smile. As the man who had made so many sacrifices for his brothers, he certainly cannot be blamed for the satisfaction he felt.

Johann had often issued pressing invitations to his brother to visit him in Linz, where he owned an imposing and spacious house, and now, in the late summer of 1812 following his sojourn in Bohemia, Ludwig decided to accept. One can well imagine his feelings on arrival and how much he hoped to find, in his brother's home, the peace, intimacy and familiar atmosphere in which to relax and heal his deeply wounded heart.

Instead—and this is where the 'satyric drama' begins—he found something quite different. He found that his brother, far from being the sole occupant of the house, was living on terms of domestic intimacy with a female person from Vienna for whose profession there is no word in the court vocabulary. As the third member of this alliance he found an adolescent girl—the illegitimate offspring of his brother's concubine and an unknown father. . . . It was, in a word, the kind of shabby situation which well befitted so undignified and shallow an egoist as Johann van Beethoven. In the complacency of his newly-gained wealth he must have become blind to the realities of his brother's character. He seriously imagined that Ludwig would tolerate this state of affairs and was stupid enough to be amazed when Ludwig not only took it as a grave affront to be introduced into such a household but flew into a tremendous rage and did his very utmost to break up the whole illicit ménage. It began with fierce scenes between the two brothers; then, when Johann steadfastly refused to fall in with his brother's demand that he put an immediate and final end to the scandalous relationship, open war broke out. Ludwig mobilised the civil and ecclesiastical authorities against his brother, receiving a sympathetic hearing in both quarters thanks to the fact that public opinion in the city had long turned against Johann. Soon it was all arranged—official inquiries having established the concubine's profession beyond any shadow of doubt—that she and her child should be packed off to Vienna in a police conveyance.

Ludwig had, however, failed to take one thing into consideration—the weapons that a woman of that type has at her disposal when she has her back to the wall. She led her lover to believe she was pregnant; he, willingly or unwillingly, fell for her ruse and had the bans called. A few weeks later they were married.

Beethoven's fury when he arrived back in Vienna was indescribable. He was raving. I had the greatest difficulty in persuading him that nothing, nothing whatever, could be done about the *fait accompli* of his brother's marriage and that he must reconcile himself to it for better or for worse. He inveighed against the laws which allowed such things as corruptors of public morals; he reviled the sanctions of Church and State which had now given the immoral conditions in his brother's home the stamp of bourgeois respectability—in short, had he had the power he would have been ready, in his rage and mortification, to smash with one angry gesture the authorities and laws which had made this marriage possible.

Thus did a campaigner for morality run his head against one of the dissatisfying imperfections which form the reverse side of all practical legislation, of all practical attempts to order the lives of human beings!

Understandable as all this is for anyone who knew Beethoven and the abnormally high standards he applied to the institution of marriage, understandable as it was for me in particular, as one well aware of his state of mind at the time he stumbled into his brother's domestic morass—I still do not doubt that all these occurrences in Linz would have taken a more moderate and rational form had not the crisis that now began in the autumn of 1812 cast a prelusive shadow on Beethoven's soul.

[62]

IN the dedicated fury of his ten-year race with total deafness, Beethoven had never for one instant considered the possibility that things might turn out other than he expected—that his powers of production might be exhausted by sheer ruthless exploitation before the event he feared became a reality. This possibility was so far removed from the mood of that unconditional resolve to which he had harnessed his whole nature and will that when it became fact his first reaction was one of blank amazement.

While grasping that such a thing *could* happen, he did not grasp that it could happen to *him*. The notion that his physical and mental powers might give out, that they were capable of refusing to obey the will that dominated and drove them onwards, was something incompatible with his experience or opinions to date. 'Strength,' Beethoven loved to proclaim, 'is the morale of people who excel'; and now it perplexed him that this simple and self-evident formula could at last have broken down.

But then, as the weeks turned into months without the source of his creative energy beginning to flow again, he was seized by a bewilderment of terrifying dimensions.

It is my duty to recount the story of this bewilderment and the aberrations to which it led. And if this bewilderment, these aberrations, had not—after a lapse of four whole years—projected Beethoven into that other spiritual terrain where his miraculous later work was to emerge, the story might have been an infinitely tragic one which could have tempted this chronicler to despair of the purpose of lofty human aims, of unflinching human faith in truth, beauty and goodness. But since that later work actually did come into existence, this story of bewilderment and aberration appears in the light of a higher logic, a mysterious coherence in which there is a truth more profound than those words 'bewilderment' and 'aberration' can possibly convey, however appropriate they may be in the factual sense.

[63]

When a simple, honest, hard-working and untalented man is plunged into confusion by some unforeseen occurrence, when this occurrence explodes his whole concept of life and, by casting him from his normal orbit, causes him to do and think things that the impartial observer may find unworthy and incomprehensible, we are merely witnessing something that has happened thousands of times already and will happen thousands of times again. Whenever such a case occurs in the uncomplicated existence of an ordinary, decent human being, our immediate reaction is one of sympathy and readiness to help. If the person concerned is at all near to us, we do all we can to assist him; we take an understanding view of his predicament; and we do not dream of condemning him as long as we are sure that he is honestly striving to establish fresh standards and to recover his spiritual equilibrium.

When we come across a genius in the same situation, we have the greatest difficulty in adopting this natural humane attitude—despite the fact that both materially and intrinsically his case has an infinitely greater claim on our sympathies.

Of all those people who were observant enough to perceive the magnitude and depth of the crisis which assailed Beethoven when his creative powers ran out—there were, thank God, not too many of them!—none had anything better to offer him than indifference, and several did not even spare him scorn, cynicism and malicious joy. I am reproaching no one. Most people are so oppressed by their own trials and hardships that they cannot be blamed for mistaking the lofty courage of a genius for arrogance or for being frankly delighted when his ship of life happens to run into rough seas. I point out this fact merely to show that at the time of his most profound and violent crisis Beethoven stood quite alone, and that no one came forward to lend him a helping hand.

As for anything *I* may have been able to do for him in those years—that is a subject I prefer not to discuss. And if I do not die beforehand, if I still get as far as telling of the last visit I paid to Beethoven shortly before his death, then perhaps a side-light will fall on me of which I shall have no cause to feel ashamed.

[64]

AND now I will confine myself quite simply to my narrative. Should there be any reader who does not sense the overwhelming pathos of the events I have to describe, then that is his own affair. But I can assure him from my grave that he has no appreciation of human greatness, nor of its perils, struggle and triumph.

[65]

As Beethoven's perplexity at what had befallen him gave way to an awareness of its full significance, he was assailed by an appalling sense of shame. He wished to hide, at all costs, the loss of his productive powers. To achieve this there was only one thing he could do: flee. He must flee from his own circle of friends, from the milieu that had been accustomed, year after year and well-nigh month after month, to receive one new masterpiece after another from his pen. He must flee abroad, get away from Vienna, seek other lands where his fame might be known but not his untiring rhythm of creative achievement. He must go to a place where there would be no one to notice if his brain were not endlessly producing something new, where no one could know or inquire too closely about his creative processes. There were plenty of capitals in Europe where he would be welcomed with open arms, where people would feel highly honoured to make his acquaintance as a conductor and interpreter of his own works over the last ten years and to surround him with rapturous admiration. As yet his hearing was not so far diminished as to deter him from taking charge of an orchestra or sitting down at a piano keyboard.

And so he eagerly began looking round for opportunities to put his plan into effect. He discussed his intentions with me quite openly, and it wrung my heart to see the helpless way in which he faced the problems that towered before him. I thought of Prague and Berlin; I thought of his encounter with Goethe and many another influential personage; I thought of his inability to flatter people and exploit their vanities to his own advantage . . . and shuddered at what might confront him once he was away from Vienna and thrown on his own resources abroad.

It may be that the anxieties I voiced in his presence and the doubts that my words evoked in him were instrumental in his contracting the partnership of which I now have to tell. People reproached him very much for this step and accused him of renouncing all artistic propriety for the sake of it—but even though it gave rise to certain events in Vienna whose recollection fills me with horror, I still feel no shame at having contributed to them through such frank expression of my misgivings. As we shall see, this partnership ultimately provided Fate with a means of guiding Beethoven through the early stages of his years of crisis and afforded him the first glimpses of the way to overcome it.

[66]

THE man concerned was one Johann Nepomuk Maelzel, Court Mechanician to His Apostolic Majesty in Vienna. He hailed from Regensburg and was one of those —by my standards—rather odd beings who only really begin to enjoy and appreciate music at the point where man ceases to be involved in its execution and the sounds of which it is composed are produced by a mechanical agency. His greatest passion was the manufacture of musical automatons. In the winter of 1812–13 he opened in Vienna a so-called Cabinet of Artifices in which, to a great public concourse, he exhibited, in addition to all kinds of technical curiosities, his new Panharmonicon, a powerful and intricate contrivance that could compete in volume with any full-sized orchestra.

Exactly when Beethoven's personal relationship with Maelzel began I cannot say. At all events it came about through Maelzel's having constructed ear-trumpets for Beethoven and fitted his piano with a kind of sonic lid, an apparatus calculated to make the already very deaf musican hear his own playing better.

In 1813 the ties between Beethoven and Maelzel became closer. The latter was a much-travelled man. Many years previously he had been to Paris and London with his various gadgets and had not failed to make the journey a financial success. Even the current exhibition of his Cabinet of Artifices was only the dress rehearsal of a big new travel project, for he intended, as soon as the Viennese public tired of him, to pack up and embark on a European tour that would eventually take him to London again. And it was here that Beethoven's plans found a point of contact with Maelzel's. Could not he, Beethoven, make common cause with Maelzel? Was this not the very man to entrust with the social and business management of his own concert tour abroad? London was, after all, the city on which Beethoven—following the precedent of Haydn—pinned his greatest hopes.

I do not even know which of the pair first thought of going into partnership—Beethoven or Maelzel—but once the plan was born Maelzel pursued it most assiduously. While he certainly expected the partnership greatly to increase the business prospects of his European tour, I have no reason to question his honest resolve to further Beethoven's interests, too, to the best of his ability. The upshot was a formal and binding arrangement between the two men, and this duly led to practical collaboration. At the end of June 1813—at a time, that is when the whole of Europe, except those parts still loyal to France, was bracing itself to cast off the Napoleonic yoke—the news of Wellington's triumph at Vittoria reached Vienna and evoked a mood of tremendous enthusiasm. Maelzel suggested to Beethoven that he should commemorate England's victory by a symphonic battle epic and compose it expressly for the Maelzel panharmonicon. He succeeded in convincing Beethoven that when furnished with such a patriotic and anti-Napoleonic piece of music from Beethoven's pen, his panharmonicon would become a sensational attraction on the journey they were planning. Beethoven agreed and set to work forthwith. I know for a certainty that he received no fee from Maelzel for this composition. Thenceforth, from the business point of view, he was already in partnership and determined to go on the European tour.

Beethoven prepared the actual composition strictly in accordance with Maelzel's specifications. Not only in regard to the orchestration, which naturally had to conform to the exigencies of the instrument, but even more in regard to the whole musical form and content: the French deployed to the strains of the Marseillaise and the English to 'Rule Britannia'; then came the clash of opposing armies; and finally a triumphant 'God Save the King'.

Beethoven delivered his score to Maelzel in September, and the latter immediately set about translating it on to the cylinders of his panharmonicon. But before he had finished—it was a long and laborious task—the Battle of Leipzig had been fought, and he fretted and chafed at his inability to exploit the popular jubilation of the moment for his panharmonicon and Beethoven's Battle Music. Feeling that the opportunity to raise money for their tour—the initial expense of which would be considerable—was too favourable to miss, he prevailed on Beethoven to re-score his Battle Music for full orchestra: it would not take more than a few weeks, whereas several months were still required to complete the cylinders of the panharmonican—and then they would jointly organise large public 'Academies' with the Battle Music as the main attraction. The first of these Academies would be in aid of a patriotic cause, all personal emoluments being waived in order to draw the public in the largest possible numbers; and only then, when the success he reckoned with was achieved, did Maelzel intend to hold one or two repeat performances whose takings would flow into the coffers of the Maelzel-Beethoven undertaking.

Beethoven agreed to this and punctually handed his

partner a new score arranged for a large orchestra and a great many percussion instruments—again without asking any fee for his work.

The first of the Academies took place at the beginning of December 1813. Its organisation was handled by Maelzel, and he proved an extremely proficient businessman. He mobilised the whole of the Viennese musical world for his purpose, raising an orchestra of quite gigantic proportions. The most prominent musicians and soloists, including Salieri, Spohr, Mayseder, Hummel, Siboni and Giuliani, considered it an honour to be asked to collaborate; the university hall was crammed to bursting point; Beethoven conducted, the audience went mad with enthusiasm, and the whole venture ended with a profit of more than 6,000 florins which were duly paid into a fund for disabled Austrian and Bavarian soldiers.

The programme consisted of Beethoven's Seventh Symphony in A major composed in 1811 and performed on this occasion for the first time; then one of Maelzel's machines played some marches; and finally there was Beethoven's Battle Music, the work originally written for Maelzel's panharmonicon to mark Wellington's victory in Spain.

[67]

AND now I would beg leave to digress from my factual register of events for a while in order to dwell on my own personal recollections of that December Academy in the year 1813.

I do not do so in order to push myself into the foreground but because I know of no other means of showing the importance of that concert in the connection I am about to relate.

Initially I had only a pitying smile for the way Maelzel thumped the big drum to publicise this event, so unusual was the sound where any Beethoven presentation was concerned. Just when the colossus who had overshadowed Europe for well-nigh twenty years was virtually laid low, it seemed, we were falling into the very error with which we taxed him most bitterly of all—that of clamour and vulgarity. Nevertheless, I told myself, the new Beethoven symphony would triumph over that, too: so great would be its power that even those drawn to the concert hall by commercial advertisement would be captivated by the integrity of its message.

I was wrong. No such thing happened. The symphony was certainly very successful, and the second movement was encored. But it was a noisy, convulsive success due more to the turbulent mood of the audience than to the true worth of the piece. And so this symphony, which struck notes never before heard even from Beethoven and which had something to impart to mankind that no musician in the western world had ever before proclaimed, passed off ineffectually. People had indeed felt its brilliance and verve; but of its spiritual and ethical content they had no inkling.

When the applause had died down, a number of attendants came on to the platform and cleared a broad lane through the middle of the vast orchestra. Having done this, they pushed forward a strange Object that had hitherto stood unnoticed in the background under a coarse linen cover. Now Herr Maelzel, clad in ceremonious black, appeared in person to unvail the Object. It was an automatic trumpeter in the form of an almost life-size wax figure with painted cheeks, long fair hair and glass eyes, dressed in the high leather boots, dainty white lace collar and broad-brimmed, plumed hat that make up the costume of a Frydlant bugler. Herr Maelzel gestured with modest pride towards his creation—and the public applauded deliriously. Then Bandmaster Umlauf appeared and took up his position on the conductor's rostrum. Herr Maelzel carried out one or two delicate manipulations in the back of his trumpeter—and, hey presto, it had begun to play. Keeping rigid time, it blared its raucous and relentless way through a series of elaborate roulades, with Umlauf and the orchestra struggling to choke down their laughter and maintain their accompaniment of the musical monstrosity.

Only now did the audience really seem to be having its full money's worth. Its enthusiasm knew no bounds. People shouted for two, three encores and showed their special appreciation when the trumpeter—covertly operated by Herr Maelzel—acknowledged the clapping with awkward, jerky bows.

I thought I should sink into the floor with shame.

At last, when they were tired of admiring the trumpeter, there was a lengthy pause which was used to reconstruct the orchestra for Beethoven's Battle Music. A vast number of large and small drums, triangles and Turkish crescents were brought in and placed in position; masses of brass instruments were moved into place; under-bandmasters took their seats; and then Beethoven stepped on to his rostum to be greeted yet again with loud applause.

His battle music duly rolled out—impressive in the majestic development of its sound effects, magnificent in its grand climax, unprecedented, if you will—but hollow and empty and futile, born of Beethoven's inimitable technical ability perhaps, but not of his talent, his soul or his genius.

Where I had writhed with shame for Maelzel's trumpeter, I now felt a surge of pain, grief and agony. The audience went quite wild and left the orchestra no choice but to play the sonorous, nerve-plucking piece all through again. Not feeling equal to this repetition, I left the hall without the least pretence of joining in the applause, my mind well-nigh paralysed by a cold, empty horror.

[68]

I did not meet Beethoven for the next few days. This was probably just as well, for I was greatly worried about him and as I should hardly have been able to conceal my state of mind, no one can tell how he would have reacted.

Then the news spread like wildfire through the musical world of Vienna: Beethoven had broken with Maelzel and they were suddenly sworn enemies. What had happened? No one rightly knew. All one could tell for certain was that Beethoven was going round his friends asking them to assist him in one or two further concerts at which he intended to repeat the Battle Music—albeit without Maelzel's 'pestilent trumpeter'. (I cannot possibly quote the expression he really used.) And it turned out that the musicians were all on his side and ready to a man to place themselves once more at his disposal.

A few days after this, I met Beethoven in the street.

'My Battle Music doesn't seem to have pleased you,' he remarked with ill-concealed aggressiveness. When I did not immediately reply, he added: 'You're the only one in the whole of Vienna who didn't like it. . . . And is that the way to treat a friend—to walk out of the hall under everyone's eyes to demonstrate your displeasure?'

'You're not being just,' I told him. 'I had no thought of demonstrating anything.'

'What *were* you thinking of then?' he demanded.

I felt a kind of wrathful indignation rising within me and retorted warmly:

'I thought I would go home before your Battle Music utterly ruined the impression your Symphony had made on me.'

Beethoven threw back his head and stuck out his lower jaw—a sure sign that an explosion was imminent. But then his mood suddenly changed and a merry light began to dance in his eyes.

'*Musikgraf*,' he remarked drily, '*Sie sind ein Kamel!* The Battle Music's a mere bagatelle'—once again I cannot put the word he really used on paper—'but at least it saves me the trouble of going to England in the company of a waxen trumpeter . . . it'll probably save me from going at all. . . .'

'Beethoven!' I cried, trying to seize his hand.

All he did, however, was to make an atrocious face at me, growl one more affectionate '*Kamel!*' and leave me standing there.

[69]

So that was that: if the Viennese were stupid enough not to see the difference between his new symphony and the Battle Music, if they were taking the latter at its face value—then Beethoven had nothing more to hide, then he could stay where he was and continue to be Beethoven in the eyes of other people. It meant that no one could have noticed what was going on within him; it meant that he could safely wait and see what would happen next.

Further developments proved him right. For what he had intended to seek abroad was now abundantly offered to him in Vienna itself in the course of the next few years. While the European armies crossed the Rhine, while the spring campaign was being fought in France, he gave two more big Academies which earned him a great deal of money and, with the steady influx of victory messages, his Battle Music won ever wilder acclaim. And as the summer brought the Viennese the certainty that their walls would soon accommodate the mightiest and most brilliant congress that Europe had ever seen, it dawned on Beethoven that he would have been a fool to try to satisfy his present needs anywhere else.

Maelzel—that unhappy, rather presumptuous Maelzel—

he now discarded with a cold indifference bordering on cynicism. The Court Mechanician, complete with Cabinet, set out on his travels without him—and when he presented the Battle Music without Beethoven's permission in Munich, the latter flew into such a rage that he involved himself in the hopeless undertaking of bringing an action against him. At the time many people strongly condemned Beethoven's conduct, and there is no denying that in law their relationship was extremely obscure, if not equivocal. I myself thought it ridiculous, and still do today, to be over-particular about the legal aspects of the matter. Before the tribunal of the intellect, a manufacturer of mechanical trumpeters has no real case to offer when faced by a Beethoven.

[70]

IT must be said here that the winter of 1814–15, the winter of the celebrated 'dancing' Congress, proved to be the outward climax of Beethoven's career. Certainly not at the instigation of our Emperor, who harboured a deep personal aversion for Beethoven, it turned out that of the brilliant gathering of sovereigns, ministers and diplomats who flocked to our capital to re-organise Europe, those with any interest in music regarded Beethoven's person and work as the chief attraction of Vienna and insisted on his being the focal point of their entertainment. He appeared in a large number of concerts and Academies before the most illustrious audiences ever assembled in one place; his Fidelio—newly adapted—was staged with unique success at the Hofoperntheater and a grand cantata entitled *Der glorreiche Augenblick*, performed before several rows of crowned heads, won him what was probably the most tremendous triumph ever experienced by a musician. For us Viennese there was a special piquancy in seeing Beethoven, on the birthday of that great music-lover the Empress of Russia, give a concert in the Burg as the guest of our Emperor—for the first and last time in his life.

But apart from these public successes and triumphs, Beethoven himself was thoroughly 'passed around', as the saying goes, in certain Congress circles and fêted in every possible way. One of the most striking personalities taking part, Count Rasumovsky, Tsar Alexander's long-standing ambassador at our Court, was his chief sponsor and promoter in this respect, and in his sincere enthusiasm for Beethoven's talent he could not do too much to procure him every personal honour and distinction in the splendid society of the Congress. As a result of Rasumovsky's attitude Beethoven actually acquired political significance, and it is a remarkable fact—also, I believe, an almost entirely unknown one—that even the completely unmusical Talleyrand made every effort to draw Beethoven into his house and parade him before the Congress. He gained only a sharp rebuff for his pains, however.

I can express it in no other way: throughout the winter of 1814–15 Beethoven openly basked in the sunshine of fame and probably felt himself a prince among princes—and I do not believe that fate could have served him better. While it is indisputable that true genius does not live or work for the present age, it is equally indisputable that the experience of fame in one's own lifetime and the homage it brings act as a healing balsam on the many wounds which self-sacrificing and sorrowful service to the spirit must inevitably inflict. I do not know whether Beethoven could have found the way to his last creative period—when he learnt to deny himself even the merest glimpse of contemporary success—in such inner peace and maturity had he not first sated himself in the experience of being the revered object of Europe's admiration. It is so much easier to renounce what one knows and has already tasted, and it is hardly conceivable that he would have been able to discern the hollowness of fame so surely if he had not partaken of it in all its illusive forms.

Most of all, I do not believe that anything but this fame could have saved him from the despair into which he had been about to sink—the despair which had already half taken possession of him when, after being failed by Astarte, he was faced with the depletion of his creative powers and found himself staring into the mocking mask of complete creative extinction.

I personally see a deep significance in the way his gravest aberration as an artist coincided with his hour of supreme triumph, in the fact that the work he wrote in ignominious betrayal of his artistic conscience brought him the ultimate and most brilliant success of his career as a composer. Those are strong words, I know. And I would never venture to use them if they were founded on my own opinion alone. I would merely ask my readers to hear what I now have to relate, and then to judge whether I wrote these words frivolously or whether I am not right to regard this coincidence as possibly the most dramatic and decisive turning point in Beethoven's inner life.

[71]

I AM concerned here with that cantata called *Der glorreiche Augenblick*, the performance of which, as I have already said, marked Beethoven's supreme triumph in his long series of extraordinary successes during the winter of the Congress.

It is most decidedly a work written for a special occasion, having been composed in homage to the Congress, to the emperors and kings in whose hands the fate of Europe had been laid. The text was provided by one Alois Weissenbach, a capable doctor who wrote poetry as a pastime. It is one of his poorest efforts. On the musical side Beethoven went in for all the expenditure that seemed appropriate to the occasion; orchestra, choir and soloists were called in and an impressive scheme of artistic effects mapped out; and it goes without saying that his score—as with the Battle Music—bore witness to a skill no other musician came anywhere near possessing. I must be permitted to keep to myself the impression this 'Glorious Moment' made on me personally—in view, that is, of what I have next to relate.

[72]

COUNT RASUMOVSKY had induced his Emperor to leave him to arrange the festival whereby the Congress was to be ushered into 1815—a year which, as the Congress thought, was to mark the dawn of a new and better era for Europe. In sheer grandeur and luxury this New Year's Eve in the Rasumovsky palace overshadowed everything Vienna had witnesses to date, for the Count put on a show which had something quite oriental in its splendour. Thousands upon thousands of candles illuminated the halls of his newly built palace, which he had stacked with exquisite artistic treasures; dancing, musical programmes, games of chance, charades, ballet and drama catered for every taste; and since even the spacious rooms of his vast home did not suffice to accommodate all the guests, Rasumovsky had had a large wooden annexe built on to the side facing the park. This, too, though it was to stand for only one night, he furnished with every luxury.

The celebration was at its peak—Beethoven and I were among the guests—when the disaster occurred that was to lend this New Year's night a fame to which its organiser had certainly not aspired. Fire broke out in the annexe which Rasumovsky had put up to increase the floor-space of his palace. Spreading with lightning speed, it soon had a hold on the main building; and less than twelve hours later there remained nothing of his stately property but blackened walls from which the naked chimneys protruded like ghostly pillars.

Thanks to the presence of mind of one or two stout-hearted men, who immediately took charge of the evacuation and prevented a panic by their firm and reassuring bearing, it was possible to guide the many hundreds of guests out into the open without a single life being lost. I happened to be near Beethoven and some distance from the first scene of the fire when the disaster occurred and we were among the first to reach the open air. After the initial confusion was over and we had put out minds at rest regarding the safety of all the other guests, and when fire-brigades from all over Vienna were racing to the scene, now cordoned off by soldiers, Beethoven took me by the arm:

'Come!' he said. And, following paths which he knew far better than I from his daily walks, he led me to a spot in the meadows beside the Danube—near which the Rasumovsky Palace was situated—where a bench beneath some trees offered us an excellent observation post. Flames as high as a house licked skywards, brightly illuminating the night; and the air was full of the merciless crackling of the fire and the crash of collapsing beams. It was a spectacle of appalling grandeur such as neither of us had ever seen before or hoped to see again.

We might have been sitting there for half an hour without speaking a word, unconscious of the cold and staring spell-bound into the blazing pile when Beethoven broke the silence. Slowly, ponderously and full of gloom, the words came through his lips:

'There goes the Congress. . . . There goes all its frivolity and emptiness. . . . There goes everything that it could have been . . . should have been . . . but wasn't. . . .'

I made no reply. What Beethoven had just said thousands of others might well be feeling and thinking at that same moment. Any well-informed person with thoughts of his own, anyone with his heart in the right place, was long aware that this Congress would be the Congress of Lost Opportunities, that it had not recognised, had not wished to recognise, its real task, that it preferred to disregard the solid bricks that lay to hand and to erect the new European edifice from rotten, mouldering débris.

Again there was a lengthy pause in which not a word was spoken. We were both caught up in our own thoughts as now and again bright jets of flame darted out of the burning palace and bathed the trees, water and paths around us in a vivid glare of light.

Suddenly I heard Beethoven's voice again.

'And there, too, goes my own self. . . .'

I glanced sharply across at him. His forehead was deeply furrowed. His eyes gazed into the distance with a strained, far-away expression.

'I have sinned,' he went on, '. . . just as the Congress has sinned. I have sold and cheapened myself like a whore. . . . I have betrayed God. . . .'

Taken completely aback, I held my breath.

'I have betrayed the spirit within myself. . . .'

Then a single, dry sob was torn from his breast. Resting both elbows on his knees, he buried his face in his hands.

I did not move or speak, but remained seated at his side. I understood what was going on within him, and felt for him in what were probably the hardest few moments of his life.

Soon after, however, he straightened up and revealed the cause of his affliction. His voice had become small and soft and sounded almost like a child's.

'I wanted to escape from the Void. . . . I couldn't abide being alone . . . alone and empty, all by myself . . . not only deserted by people . . . by sound, too. . . .'

Then he cried out:

'Oh, why is there no longer any sound in me? What have I done to make that happen to me as well? I've sacrificed everything—yes, everything—why does nothing come to me any more?'

I laid a hand on his arm.

'Everyone gets tired at some time or other,' I murmured. 'No man's energies are inexhaustible. . . . Just rest—and wait! It'll come back—I know it will. . . .'

For the first time he looked across at me.

'What a loyal soul . . .' he mused. 'What a good, loyal soul. . . .'

But it sounded as if he meant: How can *you* possibly understand!

Then he rose.

'I'm going home,' he said. 'I'm freezing.'

He swayed on his feet. I clutched at his arm and wedged it firmly in my own. Then I led him slowly back to the city.

We soon found a carriage to take us to his apartment. Beethoven, mute and sunk in oblivion, reacted apathetically. He seemed hardly to know where he was.

Not liking to leave him to himself, I accompanied him to his door. He unlocked it abstractedly, and when he stood irresolute in the hall as if not knowing what to do next, I guided him into his bedroom and helped him to undress. After he had got into bed, I wrapped him up and, without a word, sat down beside him. I wanted to be sure that he was asleep before I left.

He lay on his back with his eyes closed, and soon his breathing was quiet and regular.

Just as I was about to rise softly and make my own way home, he opened his eyes and held me back with his gaze.

And then, with the peaceful mien of one returning to this world from some faraway place, he said:

'One mustn't be a coward—that's it. Neither must one try to escape from Desolation . . . into the din of everyday life. . . . One mustn't fear Desolation, either, if it's God's will that one should pass through it. . . .'

He sighed deeply. It was not a sigh of pain, however: it was that of a man who has cast a great burden from his heart.

'Whether I live or die, now . . .' he said, 'I shall never . . . be a coward again. . . .'

A few minutes later he was sound asleep.

[73]

Now there is no question of Beethoven's having suddenly made, in the New Year that followed, any radical change in his outward attitude to the homage which was continually being paid to him. The most one noticed was that he tended to show himself rather less often in high society and, on the occasions when he did appear, to adopt a somewhat ironic manner.

Professional colleagues who tried to compliment him on his great cantata, however, were given a rough welcome from now on. Such compliments were unquestionably insincere, for professional musicians were unanimous about the unworthiness of the piece. Beethoven himself no longer referred to it among friends except by one of those verbal distortions he always loved so much: henceforth he called the *Kantate* his *Schandtate*—his atrocity.

I might mention here that in future conversations with me he never came back to the New Year's Night of the Rasumovsky fire. However, about the end of 1816 he presented me with the original score of his string quartet in F minor, which was later published as Opus 95. It bore a dedication—the first and last that I ever received from his hands—and enclosed with it was a slip of paper on which were written the almost illegible words: 'The Voice has come back. . . .'

[74]

About this time Beethoven wrote a piano sonata which was published a whole year before the quartet. It deserves special attention not only in view of its enchanting beauty but also because its composition throws a most significant light on the return of that 'voice'.

This sonata is dedicated to Baroness Dorothea von Ertmann, wife of my dear friend, now Lieutenant-General Stefan Ertmann, to whom I am indebted for the real story behind the dedication. But first I should explain that the Baroness, a native of Frankfurt, whom Ertmann married as long ago as 1798, is an unusually talented woman and was always very close to Beethoven's heart as a pianist and interpreter of his works. In the long years of their friendship—the Ertmanns lived in Vienna until 1818—Beethoven gave her most valuable and frank instruction on how to interpret and reproduce his compositions, and more than once I have heard from his own lips that no one but Dorothea von Ertmann ever really played his sonatas to his entire satisfaction.

The Ertmanns had one child, a highly gifted and sensitive boy whose frailty of health had ever been a source of great trouble to them. He was already a stripling when he suddenly died of a malignant disease—to the boundless grief of his mother, who had loved him more than anything in the world. This stroke of fate cast Baroness Ertmann into a state of dry-eyed, melancholic apathy which grew so bad as the weeks went by that her husband became increasingly apprehensive for her mental balance. It was in this distressed frame of mind that he met Beethoven one day, and when, in reply to the latter's sympathetic inquiries, he spoke of his wife's sad condition, Beethoven said:

'Bring her to see me: perhaps I can be of some help to her.'

At the appointed hour Ertmann escorted his wife to Beethoven's apartment and left her alone with him. Beethoven—so Baroness Ertmann related later—said not a word but took her by the hand and led her to an armchair he had placed there in readiness. Then he sat down at his instrument and began to play. It was not long before the grief-stricken mother burst into a flood of liberating tears—the first she had shed since the death of her child. A few hours later she returned to her husband and his love, reconciled with fate and determined to devote herself to life once more, to its duties, its pleasures and its misfortunes.

Had it not been for the deep artistic bond which linked them, had it not been for her almost unparalleled understanding of his musical language, Beethoven could not, of course, have used the medium of music to say the things that healed the sickness of her soul. But what he said to her, the human content of what he was able to pour into her heart by his playing—*that* is what worked the miracle of her cure. It must have been a very deep and valid content proclaiming things of which only the elect may know—things bound up with Eternity and man's union with God.

The sonata later dedicated by Beethoven to Baroness Ertmann is not in fact a precise transcription of what he improvised for her that day. Nevertheless—of this we have the Baroness's own assurance—it does contain, in a controlled musical form, the quintessence of what he conveyed to her in that wonderful hour. It embodies—for all human beings—the solace, the wisdom, the insight and the faith which saved Baroness Ertmann from despair and soothed her tormented soul.

[75]

I AM not really digressing here if I now invite the reader to ponder a question I have often asked myself as the years have passed: What deeper, logical reason can there have been for the way Beethoven's creative power suddenly ceased, only to re-emerge after a gap of nearly four years?

Admittedly he had played fast and loose with his energies and the wealth of musical substance that was stored in him. But physical and mental exhaustion are merely material explanations of the phenomenon; in a higher sense they cannot be regarded as anything more than a symptom of what I am really concerned with.

And if I now try to clothe in cautious words the answer I found to my question, I do not necessarily pretend to have hit upon the right one. These abstruse processes in the soul of a creative genius are far too mysterious and complex to be solved like a mathematical problem or dissected like an anatomist's specimen. I will say what I feel and think—and it may be that the opinion of one who had the deepest affection for Beethoven and was companion to the man and musician for over three decades is not entirely without value.

The reason, I think, why Beethoven's creative powers failed him was that he had already said, completely and exhaustively, what he had to say, and that for the time being he had nothing further to add.

I believe those powers re-awaked when—as a human

being—he had undergone a development which gave him vital experience and new judgement, a development which brought him into intimate personal and spiritual touch with things whose musical interpretation seemed to him to be not only possible but even acutely necessary as part of his own life work.

Beethoven never made music for its own sake. He was thoroughly unlyrical and lacked all the attributes of what we are pleased to call a music-maker. He never wrote music for any other purpose than to convey a message—his own message. And that explains why his music was condemned to silence, why the 'voice inside him' was muted, when his message seemed so completely expressed as to be incapable of further elucidation.

Thanks to the ruthless exploitation to which Beethoven—spurred on by his mortal fear of ever-approaching deafness—had subjected his energies and spiritual resources, his declaration was actually concluded and his work already in a state of flawless perfection *before* the progressive development and maturing of his human personality could bring to light the new material, the new treasures, which were to provide the substance and motive for a new declaration and a new work.

[76]

The vast difference of style existing between Beethoven's two major creative periods, that from 1802 to 1812 and that from 1816 to his death, staggering though it is in the career of one and the same composer, is something on which I need not dwell. The contrast is so great that the large majority of present-day admirers of the 'first' Beethoven regard the 'second' as a poor fool smitten down by

God and reject what he produced in this latter period as unintelligible, irrational gibberish.

But here, too, I would say this: the difference in style, however blatant it may be, is once again a mere symptom of the reality behind it: it simply indicates, with unmistakable emphasis, that the *content* of what Beethoven sought to express in his last creative period must have been a new one.

And to identify and grasp that new content is in itself neither irrelevant nor unimportant.

[77]

I HAVE already commented on the fact that the real, inestimable content of the 'first' Beethoven—the one to whom I refer as the Promethean—is a mystery to the present generation. But I have also pointed out that the generation of the decade in which Beethoven wrote his 'first' work understood him completely. Anyone with any noble feelings about him, anyone possessing an ear and a heart with which to hear and feel, understood the sublime message which proclaimed with such superlative power: 'Here is Man and here is Fate! Surrender is unthinkable! Man shall be proud, joyful, militant and ultimately victorious—in defiance of everything! Man is good and strong! His is to choose between God and the Devil! His soul is a battlefield—scene of the eternal struggle between good and evil, truth and lies, honour and ignominy—and on this battlefield alone does Fate decide between light and darkness!'

The message proclaimed by the 'second' Beethoven, however, has been heard by only very few, and the task of trying to define it in my own groping words is one that I approached with the utmost reluctance. I have no desire to be taken for an omniscient prig—but if only the present generation were not so shallow and so insensitive, how much easier this task would be!

I will make the attempt, nevertheless—in spite of everyone and everything.

[78]

THE heroism of the man who takes a stand against Fate and derives his zest for life, his faith and his idealism from the ensuing struggle is sublime and immortal.

But the soaring flight of a man's soul to a height where his struggle with Fate has no longer any meaning because the plane on which it is fought has been left far down below —that is, if possible, even more sublime, even more deathless. For it is a flight into the very heart of eternal truth; it is a flight into those places where God and the Devil, truth and lies, good and evil, honour and ignominy are no longer antitheses, where these words no longer mean anything because they are permeated by the light of the one, single indivisible Being which is the goal of our innermost longing and which all of us—each in his own way—conceive to be the ultimate purpose and aim of our lives.

This flight of the soul is what Beethoven's later works are really about. It is the meaning of the Missa, the last piano sonatas, the last quartets, the Diabelli Variations and—most of all—the Ninth Symphony.

[79]

WHEN Beethoven faced poor, despairing Dorothea von Ertmann—he the sufferer who had found wisdom in suffering, she the sufferer who had found only woe—the doors on which he had beaten in vain for four whole years flew open. They admitted him to the realm for which he yearned—the realm of light where there is no more dissension and conflict and where the pain of that heart-broken mother dissolved in an experience, an act of perception, which means deliverance to all eternity.

[80]

KANT has taught us to recognise the world, our world in which cause and effect are dominant, as a world of appearances. There are many ways in which we mortals may obtain at least a presentiment of the true world behind this world of appearances. None of these ways, however, leads further into the eternal mystery of the real truth for which we all long than music at its highest peak. The significance of Beethoven's later works, the works of the last ten years of his life, lies precisely in the fact that they conquered this peak and came to rest there for all time.

[81]

IS it surprising that most members of a generation remarkable for its lassitude and superficiality prefer to treat something beyond their comprehension as 'nonsense' and to consign it to the rubbish-heap? And since these tired, shallow people—precisely because they are so tired and shallow—feel thoroughly at ease in an uncomplicated world of appearances where everything is seen as cause and effect, is it surprising that they seek a plausible mechanical cause for the 'nonsense' written by Beethoven in his last years? A cause apparently convincing enough to demolish all arguments to the contrary? Is it really so surprising that they should say: 'He was stone deaf—consequently he wrote nonsensical music. . . .'?

Even now I can hear the angry retorts: 'One moment, my dear fellow! Did you not yourself tell us at the time Beethoven's hearing began to fail that a deaf musician is a contradiction in terms? That he was as impossible as a blind painter or a legless horseman? And did you not make every effort to demonstrate that Beethoven's unconditional commitment to music, his whole moral and artistic conception, arose from an irrevocable conviction that his life's work would end the very day his deafness was complete and he lived in a silent world? What do you say to that? Give an account of yourself!'

Certainly I will give an account of myself—gladly, in fact. For the questions involved here hinge on the very essence of music.

[82]

EVERYONE with any knowledge of the technique of composing or who has had anything to do with composers and their craft is aware that most of them have a sufficiently clear idea of what they have to say to be able to write it down in silence sitting at a desk. Mozart and Haydn, for example, never composed in any other way: when committing their work to paper, they never felt any need to check it by ear at a piano. Composers do not *have* to work like this, but most of them do so, and Beethoven did, too. From the very outset he could so clearly visualise what had formed in his imagination that his loss of hearing could not affect him in this respect.

No one is born with this faculty, which is in fact purely mechanical. It is based on experience, study and assimilation. It can be no more innate than the faculty of speaking, reading or writing. And it goes without saying that it can never be acquired by anyone who is deaf.

On the other hand, it is equally clear that no one can lose the faculty through deafness after once having acquired it and achieved absolute perfection in its use.

It would be ridiculous to think that Beethoven feared his ever-advancing deafness and drove himself to produce his first, Promethean works with such tremendous and unremitting vigour because he believed complete deafness would prevent him from putting the products of his genius on paper.

No, the impulses at work here lie much deeper.

[83]

IN fact they lie entirely in the sphere of creative inventiveness—in the sphere of its own evolution and stimulation.

Beethoven's profoundly justified fear of deafness was due not to the fact that deafness would expel him from the world of sound, from the world of what is acoustically perceptible, but to the fact that it would bar him from the world of artistically executed music—his own music just as much as other people's.

Everything new, everything genuinely creative, invariably results from the artist's having first studied, understood and inwardly digested all the essential discoveries of the past before going on to make his own contribution to the great edifice of Art in which fate and his talent have engaged him. It is hard to believe that Beethoven could have written his works without first absorbing and experiencing those of Mozart, Haydn and very many others of his predecessors and contemporaries.

But that is not enough. To remain genuinely creative, an artist must also be able to re-live his creations again and again with his own senses, to experience them again and again as living works of art, to expose himself to their living influence. Only thus can he continue to produce what is new, what is more sublime and precious than anything before. Music just happens to be the art practised in the world of sound: as long as it is on paper it cannot come alive.

It was this, the prospect of being excluded by deafness from the world of first-hand musical experience, that Beethoven feared; it was this which made him expect—with every good reason—that his creative faculties would be progressively—and, in the end, utterly—paralysed.

Nothing in the world can live without food. Nothing in the world can give without receiving—not even the richest of creative minds. Even such a mind as this is no *perpetuum mobile* but a living organism subject to the laws of all organic life.

[84]

I EMPHASISE the word *creative*. There is not the slightest doubt that the deaf Beethoven could have gone on writing as many 'works' as his hand, pen and ink would produce, had he been prepared to remain stationary when his deafness became total, or to go on repeating in new variations what he had already said before, or merely to duplicate himself. Had he done *that*, had he cheerfully written his entire sonatas, symphonies and quartets once, twice or three times over, had he diluted and repeated the masterpieces of his Promethean period—well, the generation of today would hardly have considered him a fool. But that was not to be. His whole nature, his very soul would have revolted against such a thing.

His was not merely a case of musical aptitude. It was genius.

[85]

VERY well, then—if that was the case, how was he able to continue composing after he had gone deaf? Where did his creative faculties find their food when this had been withdrawn from them?

They found it precisely in the fact that, through his detachment from the world of cause and effect, he discovered a means—in his music—of breaking down the gates which had hitherto barred his way to that other, real world of truth beyond the world of appearances.

Deafness alone, exclusion from the world of audible music alone, would never have sufficed to break down those gates. It would be foolish to assert that. But deafness combined with the force of his creative impulse and his inexorable sense of responsibility as an artist—this trio worked the miracle. They relieved him of the necessity of seeking sustenance for his phantasy in what was audible to the senses; they lifted his activity as a musician out of the world of cause and effect into that other united, reconciled world of wisdom and release from conflict, the world we feel to be eternity.

[86]

But how? He could write nothing new because he was deaf, and yet found the way to new creations because of this same deafness? Is that not asking rather too much of one's credulity?

Perhaps it is. I am not going to quarrel with anyone who —in the world of appearances, the world of cause and effect—puts the case in these terms in an effort to make me appear a fool.

Cause and effect are no longer involved here. Possibly Beethoven would have succeeded, even without going deaf, in breaking down the obstruction and leaving—in his art— the world of cause and effect behind him. I cannot tell for sure, but I am inclined to doubt it. For the Promethean Beethoven was a prior necessity for the later Beethoven— and the Promethean Beethoven is to a very great extent indebted to deafness, or the fear of an ever-approaching deafness, for the fact that he ever came into existence.

Only in the world of cause and effect, perhaps, is there anything astonishing in the fact that a man had to go deaf to become the greatest musician of all time.

[87]

This at least I do know: the Promethean Beethoven hated his approaching deafness, and the fatal compulsion it imposed on him, from the bottom of his heart. It was the incubus of his life, and it was in resisting this incubus that he attained heroic stature.

The later Beethoven on the other hand, had nothing against his deafness. It was now a friend for whom he had a frank affection. For it was the wall embracing the secret precincts in which his soul conversed with eternity and its real truth.

In these conditions he received the stimulation which enabled him to discover virgin territories in music and to forge a musical language which has the gift of expressing the ineffable.

[88]

It is not surprising that such an inner alienation from the world of triviality and appearances should have stamped the man concerned as a crank. Though it would be foolish to deny that Beethoven was an oddity in the last ten years of his life, it would be equally foolish to seek the cause of this—as most people did—in his deafness alone. I have known several men who were stone-deaf and yet far from being oddities.

During those years his neglect of his personal appearance and his unreasonable way of life came near to exceeding the limits set by bourgeois society, and anyone not sensing the lonely greatness in which the aging Beethoven lived his real, inner life might well have been tempted to feel repelled by its outer forms. A few years before his death he was once even arrested as a tramp. Setting out from Baden, where he often liked to stay in those days, for one of those long walks of his on which he was becoming increasingly oblivious of time and direction, he had arrived late in the evening at the locked gates of Wiener Neustadt. Since he had no identification papers on him and the guard took his energetic protest that he was Beethoven, the well-known Beethoven from Vienna, for sheer insolence, he had been put under arrest. Finally, when he became more and more insistent, it was decided to turn the *Musikdirektor* of Wiener Neustadt out of bed. There was much surprise and embarrassment when the latter not only testified to Beethoven's identity but reverently escorted him home and lodged him as a greatly honoured guest until the following morning.

Personal relations with Beethoven grew more and more difficult. Everything one wished to say to him had to be written down, and if the conversation interested him this lengthy procedure strained his patience to breaking point. At such times he easily became cross and irritable, and his habit of peering at what his interlocutor was writing before the sentence was finished naturally led to misunderstandings and painful situations. In brief, as time went on he found intercourse with strange, unfamiliar people an increasing burden and often even a torment.

His mistrust of his immediate associates, of servants, landlords and secretaries, was at times quite irrational, and the examples of his unjust treatment of those most eager to help him multiplied to a terrifying degree. By his cruel accusations, for instance, he drove away the loyal Schindler and was estranged from him for several years. Often enough he would forget the orders he had given the day before and would fly into a rage if anyone complied with them when they were no longer to his liking. No one had an easy time with him in those years, and every gratitude is due to all the people who persevered in standing by him and doing their best for him.

At the same time he often realised himself how difficult he was making life for others. At such moments he sincerely regretted his unfairness and his irascible outbursts and sought, by touching tokens of remorse, to conciliate those he had offended. Indeed, in one gay moment of self-recognition he poked fun at himself in a piece of music—in a piano rondo in G major which, I have no idea why, came to be known as the *Rage Over a Lost Farthing*. It is the merry caricature of a man infuriated by something quite unimportant and harassed by the petty annoyances of everyday life. For all that, it is an enchanting work.

[89]

But it was not only the irritations of daily life that were constantly bringing him up against the realities of physical existence, causing him time and again to batter against the bars of the cage to which each of us is willy-nilly confined for as long as he breathes. Serious things, too, things to which he attached great importance despite his inward flight from the world, were the source of great trouble to him and repeatedly thrust him into the banalities of middle-class life. And it is hard to say whether this is to be regretted or not. Certainly anyone aware of what was going on inside the great, lonely artist, already almost removed from this world, would have gladly seen him spared any drudgery and vexation. On the other hand, one cannot escape the impression that the existence he would have dearly loved to lead—completely given up to his own visions, secure within the impenetrable confines of his spiritual solitude—could have led to nothing good in practice, that it would have given rise to extravagances liable to prove disastrous in the everyday world. Perhaps it was better that the threads linking him with that world did not snap and proved tough enough to prevent him from drifting away completely.

The nephew Karl, that shallow and really quite negligible creature, may possibly be credited with having by his own shortcomings kept his uncle's mind in a constant state of irritation, thereby retaining him on this side of the frontier which, once crossed, admits of no return.

And so I, too, must do the ridiculous fellow the undeserved honour of including him in these reminiscences, in which, on his record alone, he should have no place.

[90]

BEETHOVEN's youngest brother, that Karl Kaspar van Beethoven who found refuge in the modest but adequate career of a municipal official, had, like the middle brother, Johann, made a weak and foolish marriage. His wife was not without means in the modest middle-class sense of the word, but she was an unstable wench—a fact which had been clear even before her marriage to Karl. He, too, was forced into matrimony on the grounds that she was going to have a child by him. Though in her case, at least, the claim of pregnancy was correct, I should not like to have to swear that Karl van Beethoven was the responsible party. I have good reason to doubt whether the same blood flowered in the veins of the rascally nephew as in those of his famous uncle. At all events, relations between the latter and his sister-in-law were excessively strained from the outset; he hated the slut, to put it plainly, and she did nothing to placate him. She remained what she was—a wanton hussy, a selfish, stupid woman who was both unscrupulous and heartless.

Karl Kaspar van Beethoven had inherited the chest complaint which was the death of his mother, and in his case, too, it was to prove incurable. After languishing for several years, he finally died at about the end of 1815, less than forty years old. The nephew was then nine or ten and at that age quite a nice—if very spoiled—little chap. Why the dying Karl preferred not to entrust him to the guardianship of brother Johann, the solid prosperity and bourgeois regularity of whose life made him far better suited to the office than Ludwig, I do not know for sure. I assume that the mother had a certain influence on the choice, for she hated both of her husband's brothers and probably expected to twist the bohemian musician round her little finger far more easily than the practical businessman. What is certain is that Ludwig himself did his utmost to make his dying brother appoint him guardian. This was just one more example of the trait which had been so strong in him since early youth—that resolute and masterful sense of responsibility for his family and its moral and material welfare. Besides, he also wished, at all costs, to prevent the child from being exposed to the influence of the other sister-in-law, of whom he had just as low an opinion as he had of the child's mother.

He took his duties very seriously, too. Childless as he was, he developed a deep affection for his little nephew, dreaming of making him his real heir and of bringing him up as an idealist and musician after his own heart.

These dreams never even started to come true. All the uncle's guardianship ever brought him was endless disappointment, vexation, grief and worry. No one knows this better than I. For the disputes with the boy's mother, who strove to make things difficult for her brother-in-law and to annoy him whenever she could, soon took on a legal character. Indeed, the claims made on the authorities by petitions, counterpetitions, appeals against decisions taken and even jurisdictional controversies among the authorities themselves—all these things extended over a full ten years or more, and obviously I was always the man who had to counsel Beethoven, deter him from rash actions and help him to compose the often tedious briefs on the case. Seldom can there have been any more foolish, pitiful or futile litigation over a child than that carried on by Karl's mother, and it is miraculous that the boy ever grew up as a member of bourgeois society at all. He went from one school to another; he ran away and was abducted by his mother; he learnt at an early age to turn the differences between his mother and guardian to his own advantage; he became an accomplished liar and hypocrite, an unpleasant creature who was ignoble, ignorant and weak-willed. Where that finally led to, what acute crisis that eventually provoked in his uncle's life, I shall report later.

For the time being it will suffice to point out that the assumption of this guardianship, apart from causing Beethoven a full measure of distress, worry, vexation and trouble, also severely hampered him financially. And that —remarkable as it may sound at first—is the only glimpse of light I can find in this whole business. For I am convinced that many a work written by Beethoven in the last ten years of his life would have lain around unfinished, or perhaps never have been undertaken, had not the stimulus of the need to earn money stuck like a sharp thorn in his flesh. There is no contradiction here with all I said previously about the metaphysical character of Beethoven's work during his last years, for by this time he was already armed against the temptation to write anything from mercenary motives that did not conform to his newly acquired standards. All the same, there was an obvious danger—as his whole activity in his last years became more and more a personal struggle with the metaphysical—that he would increasingly tend to regard the practical completion of what he produced, the actual pinning down and objectification of his visions, as unnecessary. The five last string quartets which he was commissioned to write for the Russian Prince Galitsin, the Diabelli Variations, which originated through a contract with a publisher of that name, belong to those transcendental masterpieces of his latter period which would probably never have been written but for nephew Karl and the great expense his upbringing involved.

It must not be forgotten here that since about 1815 Beethoven had not been enjoying anything remotely approaching the income which had earlier made him a comparatively prosperous man. That earlier income had been chiefly derived from the sale of his prolific output of compositions, and though the publishers certainly went on earning steadily from his works even after the source of his production had dried up, Beethoven himself did not receive another penny. And even though the annuity he continued to draw from those three great gentlemen and their heirs may have sufficed to keep the wolf from the door, it was not enough to cover the upbringing of the nephew as well. Particularly as he denied the child nothing, either for his education, clothes or other living expenses. In addition, he chose to regard as his nephew's own property a small capital of several thousand florins that he had been able to put on one side during the successful winter of the Congress of Vienna, and although the money had never been formally assigned to his ward, he never permitted it to be touched. Only a few weeks before his death, when he was lying helpless on his last sickbed, did he bring himself to draw on this capital to cover his own needs.

But sad as it is to know that a musician of Beethoven's rank, the creator of so many glorious works, was frequently in financial straits in his latter years, and vexing as it is to know that this state of affairs was the fault of a good-for-nothing little scallywag—we others profit by it in possessing a collection of works of transcendental value which but for these circumstances might never have come into being. What is more, these same circumstances tended to preserve Beethoven's grip on life and maintain his equilibrium. They constituted the dead weight that prevented him from soaring away into regions whence he might never have found the way back to pen and music-score.

With that we will leave nephew Karl for the time being.

[91]

How gladly does your chronicler now turn to another man who is likewise decisively linked with Beethoven's work and can be remembered only with sincere affection! I refer to Beethoven's long-standing friend and pupil, Archduke Rudolf, the second son of Emperor Leopold. Having been born in Florence in 1788 when his father was still Grand Duke of Tuscany, he was considerably younger than the maestro he so revered.

When still quite a youth the Archduke was given his own independent court residence, and after his musical training—his abilities being well above the traditional Hapsburg standard—had originally been entrusted to a certain Tayber, the young man subsequently insisted on having Beethoven, whom he had first met in the Lobkowitz home, as his teacher. This teacher-pupil relationship began in the early years of the century, and as time went on it developed into a sincere friendship—probably with a greater emotional emphasis on the Archduke's side than on Beethoven's, although the latter, too, was much attached to his pupil.

The Archduke deserved this. Though not an outstanding man, he was thoroughly noble in character. I have not the least doubt that it was he who decisively counteracted the considerable hostility to Beethoven which emanated from circles very close to the imperial throne and sometimes from the Throne itself. In one case I know this for certain. Once, several years after the Congress of Vienna, the Emperor had called for a personal report on Beethoven's political views, and since Beethoven was in the habit of speaking out boldly at the midday meetings in the Steiner & Haslinger music-shop, inveighing against the régime in the booming voice peculiar to deaf people, one can well imagine what the police minister's report to his imperial master looked like. Through what was undoubtedly a deliberate indiscretion, Archduke Rudolf learnt of this report even before it reached the Emperor's hands. Hastening to Vienna, he requested a private audience with the Emperor—since he was already the Prince Archbishop of Olmütz, it would have been difficult to refuse him this—and by his intercession forestalled any measure the Emperor might have felt prompted to take. If I am not mistaken, the Archduke's main argument was a tactful warning to his Monarch—and thereby to Prince Metternich—not to make a laughing stock of himself in the eyes of posterity.

It is characteristic of the Archduke that he never mentioned a word to Beethoven of the violent storm he had diverted from his head—and for Beethoven's feelings towards his eminent pupil nothing speaks more clearly than the large number of the maestro's most important works which were dedicated to Rudolf. Beethoven was always aware what princely gifts these dedications were, and he never conferred them frivolously or from utilitarian motives.

In 1819 it became known that Archduke Rudolf would shortly ascend the archiepiscopal throne of Olmütz, and it was the news of this which first gave Beethoven the idea of composing a High Mass. He originally intended it to be first played at the Archduke's enthronement, but nothing came of this, as the solemn act was long over before Beethoven had even half finished the composition. He busied himself with the score for four whole years, so captivated was he by the music and so firm was his determination not to release it until it fully stood the test of his judgement. He polished and worked away at it unceasingly.

The fate of this Missa Solemnis is rather a remarkable one. Right up to the present day it has never been performed in its entirety. In an unabbreviated form it is not practicable as liturgical music for a High Mass, as most of its individual parts are considerably longer than the ecclesiastical regulations on the celebration of the Service permit—and hitherto it could not be performed in a concert hall because in our country the playing of church music outside a house of God is forbidden by a general order of the Censor. Only once—at that great Academy in 1824, of which I shall have more to say later—were excerpts from the Missa Solemnis heard, and extremely complex negotiations with the Censor—which various intrigues served to prolong—were necessary before permission could be obtained to perform these fragments in the form of a public concert. In the end Beethoven had to agree to suppress the fact that parts of a Mass were involved and to designate the excerpts as 'hymns'. Obviously it was clerical influence which prevented any performance of the Missa outside a church, and this was not surprising. Beethoven's anti-clericalism had been public knowledge for years. He never set foot in a church—at least, never to attend a religious service—and of late he was even known to have made violent and aggressive utterances about Christ and Catholic dogma. Now that he was resorting to the liturgy of the High Mass to lay down his own religious creed in music, authoritative Church circles naturally regarded his action at best as a gross infringement.

Indeed, his reasons for doing so are not immediately apparent, and I do not think it likely that he would have even begun had it not been for the external stimulus of his friend the Archduke's impending enthronement. Once he had started, however, he was so seized by the text of the Mass and its interpretative possibilities that he became completely absorbed in them and gave not a further thought to the temporal incongruities of his action. This, to my mind, is strong proof of his almost mystical detachment from the things of this world. For he had already composed a Catholic Mass once before, by command of Prince Esterhazy, and his experiences then had taught him how dangerous it was to meddle in things of the Church. At its one and only performance in Eisenstadt that first Mass had proved a fiasco—quite apart from landing Beethoven in personal unpleasantness with the Prince.

It is my belief that the Missa Solemnis will be one of Beethoven's last works to win recognition. I even doubt whether it will ever be given to more than a select few fully to appreciate its human content, for it can never be really comprehensible to anyone whose own inner development and powers of abstraction do not qualify him to understand it. Whoever seeks to interpret it as 'Catholic' will always overlook its essential character—although, at the same time, it is admittedly not easy for the listener to disregard all the associations of the Christian Church which are repeatedly brought to mind by the text itself.

For the reason that Beethoven's religious views are not unequivocally clear from the Missa, his only work with a purely religious content, it would perhaps be as well if I were to try, in cautious, simple terms, to set forth what I know of these views, of Beethoven's conception of God, and of the ethical outlook he derived from them. Only those who are aware of Beethoven's faith in God, his personal conception of eternity and Man's relation to it, can understand what the Missa means and conceive it in its full clarity, to the exclusion of all Catholic and ecclesiastical associations.

[92]

For me, at any rate, the most astonishing thing about Beethoven's attitude towards religion was its extraordinary autonomy. It cannot be classified in any existing dogmatic or philosophical system. Catholics, quite unjustly, have many a time reviled him as a pagan, but the term is not even remotely applicable, either in the popular sense—implying godlessness—or in that of antiquity—where it is used to denote something answering to the ideals of the

Greek or Roman cults. No other doctrines or religious systems but those of Christianity and antiquity made any real impression on Beethoven; neither did he see any reason to concern himself with them. He formed his own personal conception of God and eternity, doing so with an almost naïve sublimity which at first perplexed me and later won my innermost respect. Perhaps this sublimity, which finds expression in his religious autonomy, is the surest indication of his religion's worth. I myself do not think much of religious conceptions which are burdened with difficult thought processes and logical intellectualism.

What did Beethoven believe in, then? What was his attitude towards the transcendental problems of humanity?

Now I have already said one or two very significant things on his ethical outlook. And perhaps I shall best succeed in giving the reader a resonably accurate idea of Beethoven's creed if I begin by saying what he did *not* believe in, what he did *not* find acceptable about the Catholic doctrine in which he was reared and in whose atmosphere he lived.

There were very many things in which he did not believe, and he rejected them all with a quite uncompromising finality.

Beethoven hated the dogma of the Fall of Man; he hated the concept of original sin; he hated the idea of the earth as a 'vale of tears', a testing ground watched over by an avenging and rewarding God; he hated the hedonistic dogma of an individual eternal salvation and the sadistic dogma of an individual eternal damnation; he hated the conception of the God who keeps a sort of register of men's moral behaviour; he hated from the very bottom of his heart the anthropomorphism of the Christian God, the endowment of that God with the human characteristics of temperament, intelligence and passion; and he hated all the psychological interpretations—so typical of Christian doctrine—that are based on human standards.

Nothing seemed more important to Beethoven than the

perception that there is not and cannot be anything human about God, and the conclusion from this that anyone attributing human qualities to God or interpreting God according to human standards commits blasphemy.

It seems hardly necessary to point out that such sharp rejection of any kind of anthropomorphism went hand in hand with an equally sharp rejection of any dogma, of any law, claiming to originate from God and therefore exempt from human criticism, human amendment or human correction. In a word, he hated all religious dogma based on the premise that God exists for Man and Man for God; he particularly hated the preferential rôle which Christian belief allots to Man in Creation as a whole; he hated the contrast drawn by Christian dogma between Man and the rest of Nature; he hated the view that Man alone has a soul akin and pledged to God's eternal spirit, all the rest of nature being merely a material and ephemeral manifestation of God, constituted for the purpose of testing Man and ultimately saving or rejecting him according to his showing.

Everything which is and lives was, in Beethoven's eyes, a manifestation of God and His eternal spirit; the whole of Nature seemed to him to be inspired and imbued with His breath, and he steadfastly declined to accept that Man, in his relationship and union with God, had a specific and characteristic rôle of his own as one of His creatures. While he recognised Man to be the most highly developed of God's creatures, the one most highly organised and discriminating in the intellectual and spiritual sense, he saw no reason to infer from this that human beings were subject to another divine law than that which obviously applies to all Creation: the law demanding that all things should conform in the most perfect possible way to God's creative design—that Man, therefore, should be the most perfect possible human being.

But what the perfect Man is supposed to be—that, in Beethoven's eyes, was the question which Man must answer for himself with his own mental and moral resources: the question in the solution of which he had just as little claim as any other creature to personal and direct assistance from God. God, Beethoven believed, had endowed every creature with the means of being what He intended. Why, then, should Man alone have been so poorly equipped as to be incapable, without special and continuous intervention by God, of reaching the goal He had set him? Why should Man, of all creatures, have emerged from God's hands unable to solve his vital problems on his own? Why should God have suddenly bungled when creating Man?

Beethoven was fundamentally convinced that God had not only set Man—like all His other creatures—the standard He intended him to reach, but had also given him the ability to live up to its challenge.

I shall never forget how vehemently Beethoven once declared in my presence:

'It isn't true that God made the moral laws! It isn't true that He made art and beauty! It isn't true that He invented science and all it has given us! It isn't true that He set up kings and emperors and republics! It isn't true that He appointed the Pope and instituted the Church! All these things can be both good and evil; they can serve God or oppose him. They're all the work of Man and for that reason we can only respect them where they do good and fight them where they do evil . . .!'

And when someone asked him what, in his opinion, God *had* created, he cried:

'Everything that lives! You—and me, too! So that we may be human beings—be what it's in our power to be if only we have the will!'

[93]

WAS Beethoven a pantheist, then? I leave the answer to others wiser than myself. But as far as I know he was not.

As I have already said, his religion, his attitude to God, was something thoroughly personal. His religion was his own, just like his music.

[94]

ONCE, however—it was only a few years ago, immediately after Beethoven's death—I came across an amazing book which seems to me, in many respects, to come near to Beethoven's own outlook and beliefs. I do not mention it for the sake of introducing a personal note but in order to show the individuality and the unusual strength and independence of Beethoven's views in the light of my own experience.

In a little side-street near the Stephanskirche there is a bookshop which its owner, a strange old character, has contrived to give an atmosphere all its own. Some rarity or other is always to be found there, and I have seldom rummaged among its treasures without taking an invaluable find home with me.

It was among this man's books, then, that one day, in the deep gloom of the shelves where no one ever looked for anything, I found a fat tome bearing the strangely fascinating and commanding title *The World as Will and Idea*. It was obviously a philosophical treatise and had been published as early as 1819 by a well-known Leipzig firm. When I asked the proprietor what the book was about, he eyed me quizzically over the top of his spectacles before answering.

'It's a book,' he said, 'that's far too good for this wretched age.'

'Aha,' said I, 'are you quite sure of that?'

'Take it along with you, Your Grace,' the old fellow replied. 'I'll make you a present of it. For such a book as that I don't wish to take money from an old customer like yourself.'

When I pressed him for details he refused to be drawn. 'Read it—read it! And then perhaps we'll talk about it. . . .'

The author of the book is called Arthur Schopenhauer. It is, I imagine, a name which will one day be famous in German philosophical history—though not before the present and even one or two more generations have passed into the grave.

In this book, which is the product of a quite fearless and universal mind, I found two things which delighted me beyond all measure.

The first was a language more lucid and expressive than is to be found in any philosophical work since Plato. The second was the very thing of which humanity stands in such pressing need—a philosophy which interprets the entire universe without making an anthropomorphous and personal God responsible for its creation and guidance; a philosophy which allots Man—just as Beethoven did—an autonomous rôle deriving exclusively from, and reposing exclusively in, his human identity, and which, by virtue of that identity, makes him the bearer of human destiny.

I can conceive of no more worthy or more felicitous exposition of human existence and its sense, purpose, obligations and mission. Thus far the book contains, in the philosopher's own language, precisely the same attitude towards the fundamental problems of eternity as I found embodied in Beethoven.

In one respect only do I find a substantial and, to my

mind, decisive difference between what Beethoven *was* and what Arthur Schopenhauer teaches.

The quintessence of Schopenhauer's philosophy is to be found in his conclusion that 'Existence is Guilt'. He sees life, the very fact of life itself, as a guilty stain. For him, Man's whole position, in contrast to the rest of nature, is established in his ability to discern this stain and conduct himself accordingly. From this is derived everything that might collectively be called the creation of the realm of the spirit by Man—morality, science, art.

I would never dare to come out in open debate against a man of the intellectual and philosophical calibre of Schopenhauer. I am happy to remain within the limits nature has imposed on me. But privately, in my own very modest and insignificant way, I cannot accept Schopenhauer's thesis. And I confess that I am influenced here, to a far-reaching extent, by what I know of the inner course of Beethoven's life, of the mental attitude arising from it.

Beethoven—of this I am absolutely certain—would have passionately rejected the Schopenhauer thesis on the inherent stain attaching *ex definitione* to all life. For him life was no stain—on the contrary, it was the most glorious and radiant manifestation of what he called God. Yes, one can go so far as to say that Beethoven, had he ever had a taste for philosophical speculation, would not have made any great distinction between life, the active principle that animates all creatures, and God Himself.

For Beethoven life was quite simply goodness—just as for Schopenhauer it was badness.

To recapitulate: in face of such contrasting philosophies I do not presume to pass judgement or to express an opinion of any objective value. And yet, still quite privately and discreetly, I am inclined to believe that this flagrant antithesis between Beethoven's conception of life and that of such an undoubted genius as Schopenhauer is due to the latter's being a thinker and a theorist, whereas Beethoven, with a mind closed to all intellectual and speculative theory, was a creative genius who solved life's problems in a practical and positive way.

'Sicklied o'er with the pale cast of thought. . . .' Such is the fate of the thinker Arthur Schopenhauer in this one, basic problem. It is a danger Beethoven avoided, for he did not *think* the basic problems of existence, he *lived* them.

It is possible that if I had not had Beethoven's life before me with all its significance and achievement, its immensely clear and gladdening import for all mankind, the infinite subtlety, depth and greatness of Schopenhauer's philosophy would have ensnared me in this fundamental respect, too, and made me its convinced adept. For I hardly know where I alone, deprived of Beethoven's example, should find the strength to gainsay a man of Schopenhauer's intellectual stature. But as I happen to have known Beethoven—both the man and his work—I confidently maintain that Beethoven is right and Schopenhauer wrong.

And, on the strength of Beethoven's example, I would venture to add the following:

It is naturally quite impossible to come to grips with all the problems of human existence without contrasting 'Life' —Schopenhauer's 'Will'—with 'Spirit'—Schopenhauer's 'Idea'. The antagonism between the two is inevitable; it is necessary and everlasting. It is the source and definition of all humanity.

But I question the necessity of making this contrast, this antagonism, an object of appraisal in the sense of 'bad' and 'good'. I even question its admissibility. 'Good' and 'bad' are extremely unstable terms to use where transcendental matters are involved: they are terms with which the man living in the world of appearances ought not, perhaps, to operate. I am inclined to believe that in the case of Man— the only living being to sense this antagonism between Life and Spirit, Will and Idea—it is not a matter of accepting one and rejecting the other but of *experiencing* the tensions between the two poles, of fighting them out in practice, with all the suffering this may involve.

For only thus, I feel, can Man solve this conflict—which, as Schopenhauer himself stressed, is exclusive to our world of cause and effect—and dispel it in the unity, the transcendental and metaphysical unity of the real truth that lies behind our world of appearances.

Man—so Beethoven would say—lives neither in the 'Will' nor in the 'Idea'. He lives in both. That is his fate. And this fate is good, for it leads upwards. It is *able* to lead upwards. And that is all that matters.

[95]

AND it leads upwards because it is good. In this particular respect I have not the least hesitation in letting cause and effect change places to their hearts' content. The 'goodness' of life is identical with the fact that—seen as a whole—it 'leads upwards'; and the perception that every man is at liberty to 'strive upwards' is identical with the fact of life's being 'good'.

That, in a few naïve, scant phrases, is the essence of Beethoven's *chef d'oeuvre*, the work that crowns his whole achievement: the Ninth Symphony.

[96]

HOW is it built up?

There are three movements for orchestra only: a first, main movement, a scherzo, and an adagio. And then, in the fourth movement, vocalists are brought in, both soloists and a mixed choir for four voices—a startling novelty never encountered before in symphonic music. It must have been something very special which made Beethoven resort to such an unusual device of compositional form—this same man whose artistic discipline constantly bade him keep a strict balance between the resources he expended and the weight of what those resources had to express.

As I see it, this fourth movement, the Ode to Joy, sums up the question posed by the three first movements—better still, it merges the problems presented in the first three movements into one unified, harmonious perception. Between the third and fourth movements I see Beethoven's spirit standing on the threshold which separates this world from the Beyond, the world of appearances from the world of metaphysical truth. As he gazes back at the world of appearances, he feels and lives through what the first three movements proclaim to us. They are his farewell from this world; they are the quintessence of what life here gave him; they are a complete view of life as seen through the wisdom of one who has suffered and fought through it, and for whom, as he prepares to leave it for ever, it no longer holds any secrets. And then, after one last glance, the spirit who produced this work steps resolutely over the threshold on which he has just been lingering with his memories and enters the realm of the Eternal, to be welcomed as a friend, as a victor and as a soul delivered. From there he calls back to us other men on this side of the threshold, telling us what he finds over there in that realm of unity, truth and reconciliation. He finds joy—an eternal, indescribable joy which has not only piety, humility and purity but also intoxication and blissful exuberance. This joy is the glowing flame of life itself; it is the symbol and substance of eternity.

The first movement, it would seem to me, represents everything one might call God as the Source of all Nature. The second: God as the Source of all Supernatural Power.

The third: God as the source of all Love. And what the fourth ultimately proclaims, in full consciousness of the Light beyond, is that the God of Nature, the God of Supernatural Power and the God of Love are all One. That the effect, the entity, the essence of this Unity is joy. Joy in life—the joy attained through life—the joy which is the aim and meaning of all living . . . because good can come only from joy, because only joy can guide us upwards —because life which does not joyfully point upwards is not true life.

Beethoven's spirit stood next to God when he wrote this work. His hand was in God's hand when he perceived the things of which the three first movements tell us—and his gaze met God's gaze in the moment when understanding flashed upon him of all that the fourth movement proclaims to mankind.

[97]

WITH very few exceptions, anyone who heard the one and only performance of the Ninth Symphony to date and should now happen to read what I have just tried to say is likely to take me for an eccentric old fool who, with one foot in the grave, has lost all sense of proportion.

I admit that if I had not one foot in the grave and sickness and old age had not addressed my mind to things for which one has little time to spare as long as the flame of life burns brightly in one's heart, I, too, might never have heard the message—that message of supreme wisdom—in Beethoven's last symphony. Since I did hear it, however, since I was fated to be able to hear it, I am going to speak with confidence of the certainty within me. Future generations will support my view; they will grant this symphony the position due to it and will honour it as a shrine.

But I will say this much in exculpation of everyone who failed to sense the unique and supernal worth of the Ninth Symphony the first time it was played: that first performance did not remotely do it justice. Though its composer was unstintingly applauded by a packed hall, this applause was not immediately due to any impression the work might have made—its effect had been only moderate—but to the wish of a grateful generation that this deaf and prematurely aged musician, bent by his suffering and vicissitudes, should know how greatly they esteemed him, how resolved they were not to forget him in the general degeneracy of modern tastes. Indeed, if the truth must be known, this last great Academy of new Beethoven works was not organised with any idea of inaugurating the Ninth Symphony and parts of the Missa Solemnis—of whose existence hardly anyone was aware—but to extricate Beethoven almost forcibly from the oblivion, obscurity and solitude in which he had let himself sink and to bring him to unsheath the sword of his convictions and talent once more against the worldliness of the age.

A lengthy address had been delivered to him, signed by all those older people who were loath to see a world of beauty, a musical world of the standard of Mozart, Haydn and Beethoven, overshadowed and stifled by the rubbish which even then was inundating the opera houses and concert halls—people who were not going to let their own ideals of beauty and the eternal values perish without a struggle. The signatories of this address appealed to Beethoven as the last paladin of true art, they appealed to his pride and sense of duty. He alone, they declared, could by a return to public activity behead the hydra of present-day art, so lamentable in its indigence and so impudent in its obtrusiveness. . . . It was a well-meant, stirring piece of prose as it appeared in the press, and I am only too glad to report that Beethoven was deeply moved by it.

But it was based on a misunderstanding—a deep and

tragic misunderstanding. It was addressed to a Beethoven who had long been dead. It was addressed to that Promethean Beethoven who was long part of the past, to the composer of the Eroica, the Fifth Symphony, the Appassionata and the Piano Concerto in E flat major. The signatories of the address could not know that anything new Beethoven might have to offer now would be incomprehensible to them, too; they could not know that the Missa and Ninth Symphony, when played, would only deepen still further the chasm that already yawned before their eyes—that they would bring home to everyone how unbridgeable this chasm had become.

The generation which would appreciate the Missa and Ninth Symphony had yet to be born. No one knew that better than Beethoven himself.

It had in fact never been his intention—once the Missa had missed the Olmütz enthronement date and finally attained such dimensions that it could not possibly be performed in church—to present either the Missa or even the Ninth Symphony in public. This is understandable. Neither of these works had been written with a definite, contemporary public in mind; nor had they been written to capture the Viennese. They were meant for the pick of future generations. To Beethoven, the solitary artist now quite lost in his visions, it was a matter of supreme indifference whether the Viennese of his day understood them or not.

But he himself was stone-deaf—so deaf now that, in his own words, it would have been possible to let off a cannon in his study without disturbing him. He could detect not a single note, not a single sound of what he had written. Why, then, should he involve himself in all the effort, expense and risk of organising a big concert merely to give his Missa and Ninth Symphony a life which he could no longer share?

Nor was that all. His Missa and Ninth Symphony made

such unprecedented demands on the technique and style of the performers that it was extremely doubtful whether an orchestra and choir of sufficient proportions or soloists of adequate quality could be found to meet Beethoven's requirements. And, assuming that one did succeed in assembling all these people, who would be capable of training them all in their new and difficult task?

And so there was one drawback after another—none of which made it any easier for the ageing and mistrustful man, now so remote from this world, to take a step fraught with worries and obstacles of a practical nature.

And even after that public appeal had gone out to him to come forth as the paladin of an artistic ideal that no other living man was competent to represent, even then Beethoven still laboured for months on end in a state of hopeless indecision. One day he would give his assent; the next day he would withdraw it. Time and again deputations called on him to press for an answer. And even when he had at last said 'yes' and all his technical conditions had been fulfilled, he took the least incident, the slightest recalcitrance on the part of an instrumentalist, as an excuse for 'packing up the whole affair' and wrathfully taking refuge in yet another categorical 'no'.

Refuge. I use the word advisedly. He dreaded the whole undertaking. He saw dangers and pitfalls at every turn. It tore him away from his work and drew him back into an atmosphere that had long ceased to be his own, an air he had long ceased to breathe. And only when that memorable evening was over, when everything had gone off as well as could be expected, when he had received the homage for the sake of which his old friends and admirers had launched the whole scheme—only then did the load leave his mind. As I mutely pressed his hand after the concert—I am not ashamed to say that there were tears in my eyes—he embraced me and murmured in my ear: 'Never again. . . .'

[98]

THE pathos of that evening concert was heart-rending. Beethoven himself conducted. Only for appearances' sake, of course. Behind him stood Umlauf, a competent and reliable musician, as the real conductor of the programme. None of the directions given by Beethoven bore any relation to the sounds actually produced, since an illusory, ghostly and unreal performance inside his head ran parallel with what we in the audience were hearing. The orchestra did not begin to play when he started beating time; the pieces did not end when he stopped; the choir, orchestra and soloists did not come in when he gave the sign. Not one performer's eyes was turned in his direction—indeed, they were all intent on looking past him in order not to have their attention distracted from the real conductor.

Never has the lonely plight of a man cast out from the community of his fellow beings been more drastically and gruesomely illustrated than on that evening.

After the second movement of the symphony—the powerful effect of which can never be resisted—a storm of applause broke loose: foot-stamping, clapping and cheering.

Beethoven did not notice a thing. He continued to conduct with strong, expressive movements. He was conducting music whose strains, for us, had long died away.

At this point what can only be described as an audible sob ran through the hall—an ejaculation of horror, pity and heart-felt protest at the dreadful cruelty symbolised by the lonely gesticulations of the man lost in his illusions of the platform. A disaster was imminent—an outburst that threatened to make the evening a catastrophe.

Then Karoline Unger, the eminent alto who later, in the last movement, had to sing the solo part, did something which no one present that evening will ever forget. She tugged at Beethoven's coat-tails, and when that did not suffice to bring him back to reality, she got up, took a firm hold of him and—smiling bravely—turned him round to the audience. The latter, released from its paralysis, broke out into a fresh storm of applause.

[99]

THE 'Never again . . .' that Beethoven whispered in my ear that evening was not only an expression of his will, it was also a prophecy. The great Academy of the early summer of 1824 was his last public appearance—not only because he had realised the utter futility of such undertakings, but even more because the physical effort it had involved very much overtaxed his strength.

The emotional upset which that Academy had caused left him depressed, ill and exhausted for weeks afterwards. I can safely say that he was never quite the same man again. The three—or not quite three—years he still had to live were, with intervals of varying length, taken up by infirmity and sickness and the struggles of his body against decline. The reckless mode of life in which he had persisted for so many years despite repeated warnings from his body now began, in conjunction with a progressive mental exhaustion, to take its revenge. The attacks of colic became more frequent and intense; a painful eye complaint assailed him; and once, I think it was in 1825, he was seriously ill for several months with a liver and gall-bladder ailment which brought him to death's door. In the view of the doctors, and for reasons of common sense, he ought now to have given up wine. Not that wine—I make a point of repeating this—was responsible for his liver trouble, but now that he had it, and in a dangerous form, at that, abstinence would obviously have been appropriate to his treatment—if only he had been in the least interested in observing the rules of therapeutics. He, however, cheerfully disregarded this advice as soon as his condition had improved. To what extent this was done deliberately, in full realisation of the consequences, and to what extent it was simple negligence, I prefer to leave undecided. Both may have been true. He no longer attached any great importance to life, in these last three years of his existence. He knew that he had said everything that mattered; he knew that his mission on earth had ended with the Ninth Symphony; he knew that he lacked the power to accomplish another major work. Though the idea of a tenth symphony began to occupy his mind in vague outline, it never even attained the form of a rough draft.

For all this, he remained outwardly the same. Even though his appearance, his complexion, his now almost white hair, the decline of that robust frame and the tired look in his eyes, left one with the impression of a man prematurely spent, there was hardly any change in his manner, in his temperament, in the liveliness of his speech, in the sharpness of his temper, in the fervour of his enthusiasms. The most that may be said is that he now used his deafness even more often than before as an excuse for ruthlessly ignoring people who bored him.

With the exception of Archduke Rudolf, he no longer had any contact whatever with the great world: Lichnowski, Kinsky, Lobkowitz and many others were no longer with us; and as for the new society, the society around Metternich and his privy councillor Gentz, he paid it not the slightest heed.

[100]

I MYSELF saw little of Beethoven in the last years of his life. This was primarily because I, too, hampered in my movements by illness and also living in retirement, had slipped more and more into a hermit's existence—for similar reasons, on my own modest plane, to those which caused my great friend's own reserve to become increasingly marked. I just happen to be a survivor of the eighteenth century, bound with every fibre of my being to all the greatness and creativeness that it produced—and the present era with its insipid elegance, its affected and precious sentimentalism, its romantic and false ideals of chivalry and its anæmic pallor, is utterly repugnant to me.

Nevertheless, Beethoven and I exchanged frequent letters whenever we had seen nothing of each other for any length of time. We belonged together, having formed an odd comradeship of outward resignation which was offset by a correspondingly intensive belief in the goodness and rectitude of those ideals of ours that had since been consigned to the rubbish heap. When our eyes met, memories would rise up in both of us that no one could share, and we no longer needed many words to understand one another. Beethoven's deafness created no obstacle between us. We hardly heeded it and often forgot it completely.

[101]

IT had been my hope that my great friend would one day pass quietly away from this world without any further torment from outside or within: his peace of mind, that wise understanding of all final things which was the mature and precious fruit of his spirit, seemed to offer every guarantee of this. But Fate willed it otherwise. It put the great musician, crowned as he was with the laurels of ultimate perfection, to one last, severe test—and it is my duty to tell how he passed this.

[102]

THE nephew, Karl, had meanwhile grown into a young man—and an extremely unpleasant one at that. He was lazy, vain and selfish. He fell into bad company and was soon on a precipitous downward path, the whole tone of his existence being set by gambling, women and spineless viciousness. All this was naturally at the expense of the uncle whom he was able to talk into providing the necessary money. From time to time, of course, Beethoven detected his game, whereupon a frightful storm would burst about the nephew's ears. He was only too well aware, however, that the uncle would regret his outburst before long, and that he had neither the patience nor the interest to enquire very closely into his nephew's sordid entanglements. And then the unworthy game would begin all over again: Karl, tearfully remorseful, would vow to mend his ways and expiate his past sins by making a fresh start. Fresh starts require money, however, and as soon as the uncle had paid up the same old merry-go-round was off once more.

It was all an infamous vicious circle—and however ready I may be now, on cool reflection, to conclude that nephew Karl's worthlessness did more good than harm to his uncle by anchoring him to this earth, it is still a source of bitter regret to me that at the time when I witnessed this behaviour I lacked the physical strength to teach the damnable young wretch the only lesson that would have brought him to reason.

In the summer of 1826, however, matters reached a point

where even a man of Beethoven's good nature—as far as his own family was concerned, that is!—had had enough of being fooled by his nephew. Sensing that his uncle's patience was running out and that the game which had hitherto proved so fruitful was not going to help him much longer, Karl duly gave a display of deceitfulness and blackmail which makes an old man like myself blush with shame for him.

He proceeded to shower Beethoven with violent reproaches about his alleged lack of understanding and kindness; he accused him of tyrannical behaviour and mental cruelty; and he issued a series of dark threats to the effect that his uncle would one day bitterly regret such inhuman harshness. . . .

Finally, one fine day in the height of summer, he betook himself to a popular beauty spot near Baden, where his uncle was then staying, and in some bushes hardly a stone's throw from the public path he carefully grazed his left temple with a shot from a pistol.

It was well aimed. The shot went straight into his uncle's heart, and I have not the least hesitation in saying that it killed him. The ignominy, both spiritual and social, that the nephew brought on him by this feigned attempt at suicide, destroyed his very last powers of resistence.

Unfortunately Beethoven was quite unable to see through the cold, scheming cynicism of his nephew's action and took it entirely at its face value. He bitterly reproached himself with having driven him to the edge of the abyss by his own injustice and lack of understanding. He was ready to give his own life to preserve his nephew's and pined away with compassion and remorse.

Karl was taken to a hospital in Vienna and put in the best medical care. And when it was definitely established that his life was out of danger—that it had never been in danger at all—every available wire had to be pulled to suppress a public scandal.

First and foremost the police had to be prevented from taking over the case. Attempted suicide, as is well known, is subject to heavy penalties.

Well, I was successful—thank God. And the reader will well imagine with what feelings towards the nephew I made my representations to the persons in authority in order to spare his uncle all the consequences of a police investigation. For Beethoven's sake they agreed to be lenient and treat the affair as an accident caused by careless handling of a fire-arm. At the same time, however, they insisted that the nephew must leave Vienna as soon as possible and remain away for the next few years.

Thereupon what may be described as a kind of family council took place with Beethoven, his brother Johann, myself and the nephew in attendance—the last-named now discharged from hospital and wearing a bandage round his head. For my own part, I had made my intercession with the authorities conditional on having a substantial say in any decision taken on the nephew's future—not only to deter Beethoven from any further displays of indulgence and contrition but even more because I felt him to be at the end of his strength.

Having previously clinched the necessary arrangements with a friend of mine who commanded an imperial regiment stationed in Moravia and was a staunch admirer of Beethoven, I now announced to the assembled members of the family that Karl had been accepted into the regiment in question as an officer-cadet and must report to my friend in Brünn as soon as his wound was healed.

No objections were raised, not even by Karl. I had the feeling that all three, the nephew and his two uncles, were grateful to me for having thus relieved them of the need to take a decision themselves. It was a good thing that Beethoven's deafness precluded him from hearing what I had to say to the nephew on this occasion. I told him in no uncertain terms what I thought of him, and I believe that these home truths of mine actually brought it home to him at last how shabbily he had behaved towards one of the noblest of men.

Then someone asked what was to be done with the nephew pending his complete recovery. It was a ticklish question, for it was most desirable that he should leave Vienna immediately—not only in view of my bargain with the authorities but also to avoid providing further food for gossip by his continued presence in the city.

Johann van Beethoven then suggested taking the nephew home to Gneixendorf with him for a few months. This was a remote little spot near Krems where he, Johann, had purchased an attractive farm some years previously.

Though I found the proposal extremely sensible, I feared Beethoven might veto it. But to my surprise he not only gave his approval but actually asked his brother to include him in the invitation. In response to Johann's inquiring look, he muttered the barely audible words:

'I don't like to show myself in Vienna any longer. . . .'

He was a broken man.

[103]

THE three Beethovens left for Gneixendorf in Johann's elegant and comfortable carriage, and the whole time my great friend was away from Vienna I did not hear from him. Whenever I thought of him my heart became uneasy. While I was convinced that he would benefit from the rural solitude and change of environment, I feared at the same time the influence of the lady of the house. She heartily detested her brother-in-law—with good reason, as my reader will recall—and the power that she exerted over her husband would hardly allow him to treat his brother with the consideration that his weak, generous heart undoubtedly intended.

I do not know what happened in Gneixendorf, neither have I any wish to know. It may well have been something quite trivial and irrelevant. Whatever it was, Beethoven's stay there ended in bickering and conflict. As the nephew had entirely recovered by about the beginning of December, Beethoven insisted on immediately returning with him to Vienna. And because that did not, for some reason or other, fit in with Frau van Beethoven's plans—apparently she was going to Vienna herself a fortnight later and considered that Beethoven could easily postpone his departure till then—the poor fellow and his nephew were refused the use of Johann's carriage and set out in cold, stormy weather in a miserable open vehicle, an ancient, broken-down milk-cart that made the journey a torture. On the way Beethoven was taken with a violent fever, and in Vienna he was found to be suffering from acute double pneumonia.

Thanks to the doctor's skill and careful nursing, it was possible to eliminate the immediate threat to his life, and after a few days the crisis had passed. With his temperature down, the patient would soon be on his feet again.

At this time Karl left Vienna. He went to Brünn, took up his duties with his regiment—and finally passed out of his uncle's life.

[104]

The improvement in Beethoven's condition proved short-lived. He had hardly been up for two days when a serious attack of nausea, accompanied by violent colic, returned him to his sick-bed. He was not to leave it again: the tragedy of his final illness had begun. The liver complaint which had tormented him for so long became critical, and it was soon clear that he had no hope of recovery. Angina and respiratory trouble set in, and the dropsy that followed necessitated his being tapped four times running in the next few months. I would rather not dwell on these things: it is enough to know that this long, last illness of Beethoven's was sheer martyrdom, borne with stoic indifference and as often as not with real cheerfulness.

Here, too, legend has taken a hand, choosing to embellish Beethoven's calvary with pathos and sentiment. The story is told that he died in abject poverty, that he went in need of the simplest necessities, that no one looked after him and that only a workhouse doctor came to see him now and again. At the time of his death he is supposed to have been abandoned by the world, with only a poor student to close his eyes.

There is not a word of truth in any of this. The invalid received the best medical attention; one doctor visited him daily and another, a close friend of mine, came every few days. Loving hands provided him with all the physic, nourishment and care he needed, and his sickbed was surrounded by friends and relatives. He lacked nothing, nothing whatsoever.

The atmosphere in his sick-room, moreover, was anything but depressing. Since he never complained and, whenever physically possible, took an interested and lively part in all the conversations with which we sought to divert and cheer him, he made it easy for everyone concerned to give him proof of their love and veneration.

One person who was constantly flitting in and out of the sick-room at all hours of the day and night deserves a special mention. It was a boy Beethoven called Ariel—a delightful, clever child who was never noisy but always at hand when needed, always ready to help, always on the alert to run errands and take messages. Gerhard was his name, Gerhard von Breuning. He was the well-brought-up son of a distinguished man whom Beethoven had known in Bonn in his youth and a grandchild of that maternal friend of Beethoven's whom Waldstein mentioned in his account of those early years.

The boy's eyes reflected the deep veneration he felt for the invalid. When alone with him and Beethoven one day, I was particularly moved to see with what intense devotion he treated my sick friend. The feeling came over me of being able to place the torch of my old man's love for the dying musician in those confident young hands.

[105]

BEETHOVEN had already languished through three months of sickness, and his friends had long given up worrying whether he would recover. Their only care now was that his suffering should soon be ended, for no one, neither the doctors nor the dying man, had any further hope. Then, one morning, I received news that Beethoven would like me to visit him that afternoon, as there happened to be no one else available to sit with him. I naturally sent word that I would come and, at the appointed hour, had myself driven to his home and hobbled painfully up the stairs on my crutches.

In the antechamber I was met by the lad Ariel, whom I was meant to relieve. He was about to leave for school and already had his cap on and his satchel under his arm. The invalid was asleep, he whispered, but I could safely go in and sit down in a comfortable armchair he had arranged for me at the foot of the bed, so that the patient would see a familiar face when he woke up.

'He's been asking for you,' the boy added quickly, '—but, please, you mustn't look as sad as that when you're in there—*he's* always so brave and cheerful. . . .' With that he hastened off down the stairs.

I did as the boy told me. The invalid, who was not awakened by my entry, was sitting rather than lying, supported by several pillows. His breathing was even but laboured, and from time to time there was a painful twitching around his mouth. My gaze did not leave his face as I searched in those ravaged, tormented features, already bearing the seal of death, for the vital young man of energy and talent whom I had met so many years before and accompanied up to his very deathbed in loyalty and awe. A thousand memories rose within me—happy, proud, sad and tragic memories—and in the end my emotion was too much for my old heart. I dropped my head and covered my eyes, torn by the sadness of man's ephemerality.

The voice of the invalid roused me from my reverie.

'Are you crying?' he asked softly.

I looked up into his eyes. For the first time in his life he had used the familiar 'thou' when addressing me.

'Are you crying because of me?' he went on. 'You shouldn't do that, old friend; nothing unjust is being done to me.'

Pulling myself together, I felt for one of the notebooks and pencils I always carried, and wrote:

'You must get well again, for our sake. We need you. We love you and do not want to lose you.'

He read this, and answered with a smile:

'I know that—and I'm glad. I've never made it easy for anyone to love me.'

I raised my hand as if in protest.

'It's true enough,' he insisted. 'I had no choice, though. I needed the love of all of you. I needed it urgently. But I had no time to reciprocate it as I should have done. I had other things to do—as you yourself know. I was in such a hurry. . . . I never had time for you others—never had any rest. . . .'

He closed his eyes, and for a long time there was silence in the room.

When he looked at me again, his eyes were damp.

'How is she?' he asked. 'Has she forgiven me?'

I wrote down the answer:

'She is well. She forgave you long ago. She still loves you. May I take her any message?'

'Tell her,' he replied gently, 'that I have never forgotten her. She lives on in my heart as much as she does in my work. I pray that God may be good to her. . . .'

I seized the hand that lay motionless on the blanket, and pressed it gently.

Beethoven, however, went on with hardly a pause, no longer concerned with emotion and tenderness. All that lay behind him now.

'It's not granted to everyone, when the end draws near, to spend whole days and nights reflecting whether one has used one's life properly or wasted it. . . .'

'Wasted?' I cried, forgetting his deafness.

'Yes, wasted, old friend . . .' he continued. 'The question occurs to one of its own accord—and surprisingly forcefully, too. As long as I've lived I've never had the slightest doubt that I had to make music—nothing but music and still more music—and I was so sure of myself that I brushed aside all you people who were so good to me and was rude and distant to you when you disturbed me. I was so certain of everything that I broke and trampled on the dearest woman's heart that God ever gave me. . . . But I've ceased to feel certain, now, in the darkness of the nights. . . . Do you understand that?'

'Perhaps,' I murmured. 'Yes, perhaps I understand. . . .'

'You see,' he said, 'when a man's full of vigour, when he feels his own life within him, when he wants to *live* that life with all his might—then he knows exactly where he's meant to go. He sees his path stretching out before him and goes straight ahead—drawing on the strength that is his to exploit. . . .

'But when that strength's used up, when a man can no longer produce the will to live, when his life is finished and behind him, that's when the thoughts and doubts come. . . . Did I do right? Had I the right to treat people eager to love me . . . ?'

He broke off. His eyes went dark behind their half-closed lids.

I wrote again:

'We love you for your work and your talent. We all *wanted* you to make music.'

As he read a faint shadow of mockery flickered round his mouth.

'Now you've told a lie, old friend,' he said. '*You*—of all people. You would have loved me whether I'd made music or not.' I made to rise and kneel down by his bed. But I could not: my sick limbs would not obey me. I bent my head and buried my face in my hands.

'You didn't abandon me when I couldn't make music any more. And when I made bad music you weren't cross with me because the music was bad but because it was *I* who had made it. . . . There's a great difference in that.

'Many others were even pleased about it. They hadn't been vexed by my music as long as it was good—what vexed them was that it was *my* music.

'Envy is a terrible thing. I've never understood how anyone could be envious, and neither have you. That's where you were like me.'

I did not move. I had not the courage to look up.

'It isn't as though I were heartless,' the sick man continued. 'But I felt I had no right to squander on myself all that I sensed and experienced. . . . I had to turn it into music . . . I couldn't help it . . . I should have died if I hadn't been able to do that. . . .'

Still I said nothing. What was there for me to say?

'Give me something to drink,' he said then. 'If you can. . . .'

Taking up my two sticks from the floor, I stood up and brought him what he wanted.

He drank greedily.

I shot him a doubtful, warning look.

'Don't worry,' he said, 'those medicos of mine don't mind now. It makes me feel better—and no one will benefit if I thirst to death. . . .'

He leant back into his pillows. Then he groped towards his right side and groaned faintly.

'It's often very painful,' he said after a while. 'Give me the medicine on that side-table—no, the other one, in the brown phial.'

He seemed to benefit from the dose. His features, twisted with pain a moment before, slowly relaxed, and it was apparent that he was back with his thoughts again.

'Was my trouble selfishness, perhaps?' he mused. 'I was certainly more selfish than I had any right to be. Is it really enough when a man puts art on the other side of the scales? Does service to art justify selfishness? For my solitude *was* selfishness—painful though it was to me. Can you understand that?'

He was not expecting an answer. I simply stroked his hand.

'I always thought that it was fate that made me so lonely; I always thought I *had* to be so lonely to create beauty. But often enough in the last few years—particularly now, in the long, still nights when I feel life drawing steadily, relentlessly away from me—the question confronts me more and more ominously: Was it fate? Did it have to turn out like that? Couldn't it have been otherwise? Had I—because I was an artist—the right to show such ruthlessness in never thinking of anything but myself and what I *wanted*? Was the thing I wanted really what I was meant to do?'

He was silent for a while and his gaze strayed round the room as if in search of something.

'I wouldn't have thought,' he murmured to himself, 'that a man's life could look so different when he's getting ready to leave it. . . .'

'You're distressing yourself quite unjustly,' I scribbled in my note-book. 'You life was one of grandeur and clarity. I know, we all know.'

He read what I had written.

'Yes!' he cried eagerly. 'Yes! I've often felt *that*, too, in these long nights—and then there seemed to be a sea of light and happiness around me, and I prayed to be allowed to die amid that blaze of light—but it wasn't yet time. . . .'

A radiant look came into his eyes.

'And I believe . . . I believe I have found what it is that comforts me. . . .'

Propping himself on both hands, he struggled into a sitting position, taking one or two deep breaths as if to bring fresh power to his heart. As he began to speak again, his voice had almost the firm, old ring of the days when he had been well.

'I never searched just for beauty, just for music—I sought the *truth* hidden behind beauty—and that's why, perhaps, it was permissible for me to be so hard and selfish and why my hardness and selfishness will perhaps be forgiven. . . .

'What *is* truth, though?

'I believe truth is what we humans can only seek but never find—and to have sought it is the utmost that can ever be granted to a man. . . .

'To look *behind* things, to look past them and through them, not to try to understand one thing alone but what lies behind *all* things—*that's* what truth is—and it may be that the only way I could seek this truth—the truth we can never reach but only long for—was in my music. . . .'

His body drooped slightly, and he closed his eyes.

'The brook . . . you know, in my Pastoral Symphony. . . .

I heard its murmur last night, in my fever. . . . And then I understood that my music hasn't just caught *one* brook—it's caught the murmur of all the brooks in the world: it wasn't just my own interpretation that I put to music, it was that of *all* men who have ever sensed God and the eternal beauty of life at the side of a blissfully bubbling brook. . . .

'And my love—my belief—my courage—my sincerity and anger—my despair, my fear—my whole vigour—everything I have ever experienced or felt—everything I have ever made into music through ruthless selfishness, simply because music happened to be the only language I could speak—perhaps all these things were not only *mine*—perhaps they were also the love, belief and fortitude of all living people—because I was always in search of truth and because beauty, for me, only existed as a means of attaining truth, attaining what lies *behind* everything. . . .'

His voice had been sinking lower and lower. I sensed that he had forgotten me, that he was alone with himself—alone with eternity—hardly in this world any longer.

'Life is a hard trial,' he whispered to himself. 'It *compels* a man, it drives him forward—it's full of such grim, bitter struggle. . . . He climbs to celestial heights—and plunges into the abyss of hell. . . . And when he awakes, what then? That's when he understands that in all he did and suffered, in all the good and bad things he inflicted upon himself and other people, he was only wandering—groping—fumbling . . . like a blind man feeling his way with a stick. Then he understands that only *one* thing was good, only *one* thing had any value, sense or purpose—the fact that he searched for God, often without knowing it. . . .'

Suddenly he opened his eyes wide and fixed them imploringly on mine.

'It isn't the fact that I made music,' he cried, 'it isn't *that* which justifies me—anyone with the proper talent can do the same—just as the blacksmith forges his horseshoe and the joiner makes his table. It isn't the horseshoe or the table or the music that counts! The only thing that counts is that the blacksmith should make his horseshoe as perfect as possible, that he should tirelessly strive to make it better and better! *That's* the way to truth—the only way. . . .

'God knows there was nothing in the world I could do half as well as make music—and I only did so because I did it well, not because I was vain or because it flattered me to be admired and to achieve more than others. . . . No, only because I could make music better than anything in the world . . . because only in music could I seek perfection. . . .

'Perfection! That's what justifies a man—in all his obduracy, in all his selfishness, in all his self-regard.

'Anyone who has persistently sought perfection, anyone who has sought himself for the sake of that perfection—that man has done the utmost that can be granted to a man to do. For close behind perfection, well within reach—believe what I am telling you, old friend—stands truth—the truth which turns a single thing into *all* things, a single being into *all* beings. . . .'

The intense excitement which had seized him suddenly subsided. He sank back exhausted—only to rear up again in violent dismay.

'Oh,' he groaned, 'I feel so sick. . . .'

I helped as best as I could. I supported him as he fought laboriously for breath, laying my arm round his shoulders; I wiped away the huge beads of sweat that had come out on his brow. Slowly, very slowly, he rallied. His breathing became more regular, and the cramp in his body passed away.

'It's better now,' he said, '. . . thank you.'

And as I eased him back into his pillows, he beckoned to me to sit down beside him again.

He took my hand and held it tight.

'It's good that you're here . . . I thought the end was

coming. . . . Stay with me . . . perhaps I can sleep a little. . . .'

His eyes closed.

Before long I felt his hand go slack in mine, slowly detaching itself to drop heavily on to the blanket.

[106]

Two hours later the door opened. I gently raised my hand in warning: The invalid was still sleeping peacefully.

Then I rose and, with one last, long look at that beloved face, I left my dying friend.

It was the last time I ever saw him alive.

EPILOGUE

Nothing is further from the minds of the publisher or the author of this book than to subject the reader to another of those literary deceptions which used to be so popular. Nikolaus Zmeskall von Domanovetz never did write any reminiscences of Beethoven, and the fact that the author has chosen to undertake this biographical sketch of the composer in the form of fictitious memoirs ostensibly emanating from Domanovetz's pen is due to considerations with which he now proposes to deal in absolute frankness.

The first thing to bear in mind is that any new book on Beethoven must contain its own *raison d'être*. For this it can never rely on mere factual content but only on its *interpretive* treatment of the musician's life. The purely factual aspects already fill entire libraries—libraries which, apart from a great deal of palpable rubbish and worse, contain a wealth of most valuable material, selected and compiled with the utmost accuracy, diligence and devotion. Nevertheless, it would appear that no really successful attempt has ever been made to produce a biography of Beethoven which, though neither a musicological study nor a literary essay, was actually both of these at once—in other words, a life of Beethoven which, while paying the strictest regard to historical fact, made use of a literary form which could give the non-specialist reader a durable picture of the great musician.

What, then, was to stop one from simply writing a *novel* about Beethoven? A work so conceived that the author played the rôle of one who knew and understood everything there was to know about the composer's life? The answer, quite simply, is that modesty, awe and respect precluded it. A writer may do what he likes with figures of his own invention but not with the flesh and blood of historical personalities of great significance to mankind. Such was the author's view, and he could never even have contemplated that identification of self and subject on which the success of any 'objective' novel depends—least of all when his hero's name was Beethoven.

In brief, the author sought a literary pattern which would compel him to subject himself, his factual knowledge and his personal views and feelings about Beethoven to certain strict limitations. Hardly anything can be more conducive to objectivity in a writer than having to force all he knows and has to say about a particular subject through the filter of another personality outside himself. By this device, which is, of course, not at all new, the portrayal in question is no longer arbitrary and is lent credibility not only by care in the use of technical data but most of all by the inner logic and consistency of the 'filter-personality' employed.

It is not intended to do anything more than hint at the laws and relative forces at work here—but in the present case the device of the author's choosing may perhaps be considered especially justified by the fact that Nikolaus von Zmeskall's personality is quite admirably—not to say provocatively—suited to it. Zmeskall was indeed everything the author makes him out to be. He was a first-rate musician who played the 'cello exceptionally well and composed a number of string quartets which are rated far above the average by competent judges; he is the only one of Beethoven's friends whose life ran consistently parallel with that of the great composer throughout his years in Vienna; he was some ten years older than Beethoven and survived him by six years. But what contributed more than anything to the author's decision to make Zmeskall his narrator was the fact that from Beethoven's earliest days in Vienna right up to his death the real Zmeskall was always the same equable friend to him, ever ready with a helping hand. Of all the people who appeared for any appreciable length of time in Beethoven's life, he is—quite literally—the only one with whom Beethoven never fell out for so much as a single moment. This could never have been so had that modest court official not harboured a deep, respectful and lofty affection for the great artist—an affection which, thanks to his veneration of the other's genius, could put up with all those rough corners and edges to Beethoven's character against which no other man's self-esteem and sense of proportion were proof.

So if the author preferred to violate the historical Zmeskall by ascribing to him memoirs which he did not write rather than to run the unjustifiable risk of producing a 'direct' account of Beethoven's life, it may be that he has rendered historical truth the additional service of raising a modest memorial to that extraordinarily sympathetic character, Nikolaus Zmeskall von Domanovetz. Goodness knows that all Zmeskall did for Beethoven makes him deserving of a little limelight for once.

The author begs leave to point out that the above work was conceived and put on paper in the year 1943.

Ehrwald, 1949